INTERSCIENCE TRACTS ON PHYSICS AND ASTRONOMY

Edited by R. E. Marshak
University of Rochester

Additional volumes in preparation

QC /
I 4
physics

10/7/63
S. D.

THE NUCLEON-NUCLEON INTERACTION

Experimental and Phenomenological Aspects

RICHARD WILSON

Professor of Physics, Harvard University,
Cambridge, Massachusetts

INTERSCIENCE PUBLISHERS
a division of John Wiley & Sons, New York • London

Preface

There seems to be no book, and indeed no review, discussing the nucleon-nucleon interaction from an experimenter's point of view. In my instruction of graduate students, I have often wished for one.

Now seems a good time for writing such a book. The experimental data give quite a complete general picture of the interaction from a phenomenological point of view. A new era of refinement in experiments is necessary to answer the more detailed questions that we can now pose.

The time is convenient for myself also; my first experiments in physics were on this subject (Bishop 1950), and I am now leaving this field. It is not unnatural, therefore, that I refer frequently to the works of my collaborators and myself in the field—collaborators at Oxford, AERE Harwell, and now at Harvard. To these collaborators and, in particular, to Prof. H. Halban and Dr. C. H. Collie who introduced me to the subject, must go much of the credit for this book.

I wish to acknowledge helpful comments and criticism from Professors Feshbach, Palmieri, Tinlot, Noyes, and Moravcsik, who have prevented this book from having more mistakes than it has.

RICHARD WILSON

Cambridge, Mass.
June 1962

Contents

Chapter 1

Introduction and
Historical Background

The electric forces between charged particles are well known and obey the simple force law enunciated by Coulomb. When magnetism is included, electromagnetic forces are only a little more complex and are easily described by the electric and magnetic fields as shown by Maxwell. At the turn of the twentieth century the forces were thus well known, but the basic mechanics of the particle motions was unknown. Classical mechanics was inadequate. However, the belief in the validity of the basic forces enabled the theory of quantum electrodynamics to be developed and tested.

With nuclear forces the situation is inverted. Quantum mechanics is accepted, but the laws governing the forces are still badly understood. The nucleon is an elementary particle in the sense that a simpler description cannot be given in terms of its constituents. It is complex, however, in the sense that it is strongly coupled to the meson field and the interactions automatically involve the properties of mesons. The theory of these processes is mathematically difficult. It is necessary to measure the interaction between nucleons in detail for comparison with theory. It is the purpose of this book to outline the procedures involved in this measurement. A companion volume by H. P. Noyes will discuss the theoretical calculations of the interaction. This does not mean that in this book I shall be content to describe the obtaining of cross sections. They must be correlated sufficiently by a phase shift or other analysis, so that they may be meaningfully discussed. Other theoretical books

1

and reviews are frequent. Useful ones include Moravcsik (1963), Bethe (1948), Hulthèn (1957), Blatt (1952), Sachs (1955), Gammell (1959), MacGregor (1960), Wolfenstein (1956), Breit (1953, 1962).

The first clear picture of the atomic nucleus was given in 1911 by Rutherford's celebrated experiments on the scattering of α particles by heavy elements. He showed that there is a positively charged atomic nucleus many times smaller than the atomic size. Measurements of x-ray spectra were interpreted with the recent Bohr theory of the atom by Moseley to show that the positive charge was exactly equal to the atomic number of the element. The atomic nucleus was imagined to be a collection of protons plus enough neutral particles, or complexes, to make up the atomic weight. The discovery of the neutron by Chadwick in 1932 showed the nature of the neutral particle.

The forces binding the nucleons together to form the nucleons are attractive and stronger than the Coulomb force, but must be of short range so that the Coulomb force can predominate at large nucleon separations. Another difference from Coulomb forces is quickly apparent. Charges attract (or repel) all other charges in their vicinity. The forces binding an atom together become much stronger when the number of charges increases, so that the size of the atom does not rise as fast as the number of charges.

By contrast, the forces binding a nucleus do not appear to increase as the size of the nucleus increases. A saturation appears after four nucleons (the helium nucleus) and the radius of the nucleus becomes proportional to $A^{\frac{1}{3}}$ (volume proportional to A). The mass defect of the nucleus does not continually increase as might be expected if no saturation occurred.

The short range nature of the force was made most certain by the discovery of the deuteron—the most elementary of the nuclei and the most lightly bound. The fact that the deuteron binding energy (2.225 mev) is small compared with the binding energy of the α particle (25 mev) is used by Wigner as evidence to show that the nuclear forces have a smaller range than the deuteron size—an important fact for the theory, and also for the validity of the impulse approximation which is used to analyze many of the experiments to be described.

That nuclear forces are spin dependent was first made clear by the spectroscopic observation that the deuteron has spin 1, corresponding to an addition of the spins of the neutrons and protons, and the later confirmation that there is no bound state of spin 0.

In the years 1933–1939 the information rapidly accumulated. Proton-proton scattering was first performed by Wells, and precise numbers obtained by Tuve (1936) at 600–900 kev; like the earlier α particle scattering experiments on nuclei, a deviation from the prediction of the Coulomb force law was found which showed that there was an attractive interaction, stronger than the Coulomb interaction at small separations.

Chadwick and Goldhaber (1935) irradiated deuterium with γ rays of energy 2.618 mev, and measured the protons (of energy 196 kev) from the disintegration according to the reaction

$$\gamma + d \rightarrow n + p \tag{1-1}$$

This was combined with the mass spectroscopic data on the mass difference

$$2M_p - M_D \tag{1-2}$$

to give the first accurate measurement of the binding energy of the deuteron. According to the theory of the next chapter, the process is expected to proceed by an electric dipole transition (for magnetic dipole reactions are usually found to be smaller). The cross section should therefore vary as the $\frac{3}{2}$ power of the excess of the gamma-ray energy over threshold $(E_\gamma - \epsilon)^{3/2}$.

Amaldi and Fermi (1936) measured the capture cross section of "thermal" neutrons by hydrogen, which is the inverse reaction and related by the theory of detailed balancing. The cross section was found to be a hundred times larger than that predicted by the above energy dependence. This was explained by considering the spin dependence of the nuclear forces; if the reaction (1-1) proceeds by a magnetic dipole transition the neutron-proton system has angular momentum 0; if the neutron and proton attract each other in this state the transition would be enhanced. This occurs at the (virtual) singlet state of the neutron-proton system. The triplet interaction has, of course, a real bound state—the deuteron.

The spin dependence of nuclear forces was further confirmed by measuring the coherent scattering of neutrons by hydrogen containing molecules. The scattering cross section, for example, was found to be different for orthohydrogen where the two protons are in a triplet state, from that in parahydrogen where they are in a singlet state. The scattering from hydrogen atoms coherently oriented in crystals is also different from that from free hydrogen atoms. The coherent scattering of neutrons from hydrogenous liquids, which is now the best measurement of this effect, will be more fully described in the next chapter.

Coulomb forces are directed along the line joining the two charges and are said to be "central" forces. The same is not completely true of nucleon-nucleon forces. The first proof of this was the discovery of the quadrupole moment of the deuteron (Kellogg, 1939). This shows that the deuteron is not spherically symmetric. Such a deviation from spherical symmetry can only arise from the existence of the preferred direction given by the deuteron spin. This suggests searching for other effects. It is found that the magnetic moment of the deuteron is not quite equal to the sum of those of the proton and neutron

$$\mu_d = 0.8574 \text{ nuclear magnetons}$$

$$\mu_n + \mu_p = 0.8791 \text{ nuclear magnetons} \qquad (1\text{-}3)$$

This was the status of the field in 1939. The stage was set for a systematic unifying theoretical treatment. This was already partially done by Bethe, Breit, and others.

In the pages which follow, this development will be outlined. In Chapter 2, the theory of the deuteron will be outlined together with the effective range theory for low interactions and the relevant low-energy experiments. These low-energy experiments are very precise but can give only limited information. The parameters obtained in this section are the "best" parameters as of June 1, 1962, and are more precise than those available hitherto.

Chapters 3 to 6 discuss the high-energy experiments. An arbitrary limitation to elastic scattering is here imposed, and this effectively limits the book to energies below 400 mev. For the sake of completeness, however, experiments at higher energies are included in the tables.

The variety of experiments that it is theoretically possible to perform is discussed in Chapter 3, together with a general statement of the "complete set" of experiments which is adequate if time reversal and parity invariance are assumed. In Chapter 4 the available experimental techniques are described and Chapters 5 and 6 discuss the proton and neutron experiments, respectively.

In Chapter 7 the analysis of the experiments is pursued. The usual representation of the data in terms of phase shifts is used, and the results are collected into some phases at certain energies.

In Chapter 8 the radiative processes, in particular electron-deuteron scattering, are discussed and analyzed in the same effective range theory as used in Chapter 2.

In Chapter 10, the framework for using these results for the more complex processes of elastic scattering by nuclei is discussed.

Low-Energy Theory and Experiment

2.1 The Deuteron Ground State

We start first with the theory of the ground state of the deuteron. This will be treated here in the approximation that forces are purely central (Bethe, 1935). The Schroedinger equation for the relative motion of the neutron and proton of separation r is

$$(-\hbar^2/M)\nabla^2\psi(r) + V(r)\psi(r) = E\psi(r) \qquad (2\text{-}1)$$

(Note that M is twice the reduced mass)

The ground state in this approximation is spherically symmetric, and we put $\psi = (1/\sqrt{4\pi})N_g u_g(r)/r$. Then $[N_g u_g(r^2)]^2 dr$ is the probability of finding the two particles between r and $r + dr$. The normalization constant N_g is such that

$$\int (\psi(r))^2 d\mathbf{r} = 1 \quad \text{and} \quad \int_0^\infty u_g^2(r)dr = 1/N_g^2$$

We will later [equation (2-22)] define a convenient normalization for $u_g(r)$. Till then, N_g is arbitrary.

Then $u(r)$ obeys a simpler equation

$$-\frac{\hbar^2}{M}\frac{d^2 u_g}{dr^2} + V(r)u_g(r) = Eu(r) \qquad (2\text{-}2)$$

We are interested in a solution of this equation for an energy E equal to $-\epsilon$, where ϵ is the binding energy of the deuteron. Now

7

for large distances $V(r)$ is negligible. We are interested in a bound state for which $u(r) \to 0$ as $r \to \infty$ and, to keep ψ finite at the origin, $u_g = 0$ at $r = 0$. As $r \to \infty$, $u_g(r)$ must tend to a form v_g given by

$$v_g = Ae^{-\gamma r} \tag{2-3}$$

where A is a normalizing constant defined to be unity, and

$$\gamma^2 = M\epsilon/\hbar^2 \tag{2-4}$$

$1/\gamma$ is sometimes called the radius of the deuteron and equals 4.3×10^{-13}. The solution $Be^{+\gamma r}$ is excluded by the boundary condition at infinity.

2.2   Neutron–Proton Scattering, Partial Wave Analysis. Rayleigh (1877), Mott (1933)

At large distances $(r \to \infty)$ from the center of mass of the neutron-proton system the wavefunction $\psi(r) = \psi(x, y, z)$ has the form

$$\psi(r) \cong \exp{(ikz)} + f(\theta) \, [\exp{(ikr)/r}] \tag{2-5}$$

where the second term is the scattered wave. The wave number k is given at large r by the requirement that $\psi(r)$ be a solution of (2-1). Then $k = [ME/\hbar^2]^{1/2}$. The differential cross section for a scattering into a solid angle $d\Omega$ is given by

$$d\sigma/d\Omega = |f(\theta)|^2 \tag{2-6}$$

The equation (2-1) may now be solved in spherical polar coordinates. It is easily seen that

$$\psi = P_l(\cos\theta)u_l(r)/r \tag{2-7}$$

where

$$\frac{d^2u_l}{dr^2} + k^2 \left[1 - V/E - \frac{l(l+1)}{k^2r^2} \right] u_l = 0 \tag{2-8}$$

The appearance of the "centrifugal barrier" $l(l + 1)/r^2$ is now observed. The boundary conditions are now only that $u = 0$ at $r = 0$. We see

$$u(r) \rightarrow B \sin (kr + \delta) \quad \text{as} \quad r \rightarrow \infty \tag{2-9}$$

In the absence of a potential, $u(r) \rightarrow B \sin (kr)$. δ is called the *phase shift*.

We are here only concerned with the asymptotic forms which we therefore derive

$$\psi(r) = \sum_0^\infty (2l + 1)i^l e^{i\delta_l} P_l(\cos \theta) \tag{2-10}$$

and the asymptotic form for the scattered wave

$$f(\theta) = \frac{1}{2ik} \sum_{l=0}^\infty (2l + 1)[e^{2i\delta_l} - 1]P_l(\cos \theta)$$

$$= \frac{1}{k} \sum_{l=0}^\infty (2l + 1) \sin \delta_l e^{i\delta_l} P_l(\cos \theta) \tag{2-11}$$

$f(\theta)$ is thus, in general, complex.

The cross section is $|f(\theta)|^2$. When integrated over all angles the cross terms in $P_l(\cos \theta)P_m(\cos \theta)$ vanish and the result becomes

$$\sigma = \frac{4\pi}{k^2} \sum_{l=0}^\infty (2l + 1) \sin^2 \delta_l \tag{2-12}$$

This separation of the scattering amplitude $f(\theta)$ into the partial waves of different angular momentum is general, relativistically covariant, and independent of the potential assumed. It is, therefore, a convenient parameterization of the experiments.

At low energies, we expect only $S(l = 0)$ waves to be of importance, and we accordingly deduce the phase shift δ_0 from the wave equation (2-2). For $E = 0$, the solution $u_0(r)$ as $r \rightarrow \infty$ becomes $d^2u_0/dr^2 = 0$, i.e., $u_0(r)$ becomes a straight line. At $r = 0$, $u_0 = 0$ as before. Since $u_0(r)$ has an undetermined normalization, the only significant feature is the value of r (other than $r = 0$) for which $u_0(r) = 0$. This value $r = a$ is defined as the *scattering length*.

$$\therefore \ u_0(r) \ \rightarrow \ C(1 - r/a) \qquad (2\text{-}13)$$

from equation (2-9), we have for $k \rightarrow 0$

$$u_0(r) \ \rightarrow \ B(kr \cos \delta + \sin \delta) \quad \text{as} \quad r \rightarrow \infty \qquad (2\text{-}14)$$

Equating powers of r we find

$$\tan \delta \ \rightarrow \ -ka \quad \text{for} \quad k \rightarrow 0 \qquad (2\text{-}15)$$

Hence the scattering cross section at zero energy becomes

$$\sigma = 4\pi a^2 \qquad (2\text{-}16)$$

2.3   Effective Range Expansion

This was first derived by Schwinger (1947) but we follow here the treatment of Bethe (1949)(1950); see also Lippmann (1950), Blatt (1949), Chew (1949), and Hulthén (1957).

We have the equation (2-2) for an energy E_1

$$-(\hbar^2/M)(d^2u_1/dr^2) + V(r)u_1(r) = E_1(r)u_1(r) \qquad (2\text{-}17)$$

and for energy E_2

$$-(\hbar^2/M)(d^2u_2/dr^2) + V(r)u_2(r) = E_2(r)u_2(r) \qquad (2\text{-}18)$$

We multiply (2-17) by u_2, and (2-18) by u_1 and subtract (2-17) from (2-18) to yield

$$d/dr(u_1u_2' - u_2u_1') = (k_2{}^2 - k_1{}^2)u_1u_2 \qquad (2\text{-}19)$$

where the prime denotes differentiation. We now define the asymptotic forms v_1 and v_2 such that $u_1 \rightarrow v_1$ as $r \rightarrow \infty$

$$d/dr(v_1v_2' - v_2v_1') = (k_2{}^2 - k_1{}^2)v_1v_2 \qquad (2\text{-}20)$$

We subtract (2-20) from (2-19) and integrate over r from 0 to ∞. Then

$$v_1(0)v_2'(0) - v_2(0)v_1'(0) = (k_2{}^2 - k_1{}^2)\int_0^\infty (u_1u_2 - v_1v_2)dr \quad (2\text{-}21)$$

since $u_1(0) = u_2(0) = 0$ and $u_1(\infty) = v_1(\infty)$.

If we now take as the normalization of the wavefunction $v_j(0) = 1$, in the same way that we took $v_g(0) = 1$ in (2-3), then

$$v_j(r) = \frac{\sin (k_j r + \delta_j)}{\sin \delta_j} \quad (2\text{-}22)$$

where the suffix j here denotes the energy and *not* the angular momentum which is zero. Then

$$k_2 \cot \delta_2 - k_1 \cot \delta_1 = (k_2{}^2 - k_1{}^2)\int_0^\infty (v_1v_2 - u_1u_2)dr \quad (2\text{-}23)$$

We define

$$\tfrac{1}{2}\rho(E_1, E_2) = \int_0^\infty (v_1v_2 - u_1u_2)dr \quad (2\text{-}24)$$

which has the dimensions of a length; ρ is called the *effective range*. Then

$$k \cot \delta = [k \cot \delta]_{k=0} + \tfrac{1}{2}k^2\rho(0, E) \quad (2\text{-}25)$$

$$= -1/a + \tfrac{1}{2}k^2\rho(0, E) \quad \text{from (2-15)} \quad (2\text{-}26)$$

It is clear from the definition that $\rho(0, E) = \rho(E, 0)$. The total S-wave scattering cross section is then given by

$$\sigma = \frac{4\pi}{k^2 + [\tfrac{1}{2}k^2\rho - 1/a]^2} \quad (2\text{-}27)$$

Equations (2-26) and (2-27) are exact. The approximation comes in observing that if the range of forces is small, then $\rho(E_1, E_2)$ does not depend critically on E_1 and E_2 and can be treated as a constant

r_0 called the effective range. (In the literature r_0 is usually defined as $\rho(0, 0)$ in our notation. This is not a very useful quantity.) Figure 2-1 shows a graphical plot of u_g, u_0, v_g, v_0. The shaded area is 2ρ. That it is not critically dependent on energy is at once clear.

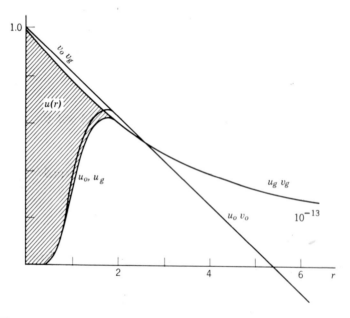

Figure 2-1. A graphical plot (not to scale) of the deuteron ground state wavefunction u_g and its asymptotic form v_g and the zero energy wavefunctions u_0 and v_0.

We now extend (2-26) to the ground state of the deuteron using (2-3) and (2-4).

$$v_g'(0) = -1/a - \tfrac{1}{2}\gamma^2\rho(0, -\epsilon) \qquad (2\text{-}28)$$

$$\gamma = 1/a + \tfrac{1}{2}\gamma^2\rho(0, -\epsilon) \qquad (2\text{-}29)$$

which is still exact.

From the usual normalization, $N_g{}^2 \int_0^\infty u_g{}^2 dr = 1$ we can derive $N_g{}^2$

$$1/N_g{}^2 = \int_0^\infty u_g{}^2 dr = \int_0^\infty v_g{}^2 dr - \int_0^\infty (v_g{}^2 - u_g{}^2) dr \quad (2\text{-}30)$$

$$= \frac{1}{2\gamma} - \frac{1}{2} \rho(-\epsilon, -\epsilon) \quad (2\text{-}31)$$

$$N_g{}^2 = \frac{2\gamma}{1 - \gamma\rho(-\epsilon, -\epsilon)} \simeq \frac{2\gamma}{1 - \gamma r_0} \quad (2\text{-}32)$$

Thus any measurement of the asymptotic deuteron ground state wavefunction gives the effective range and vice versa.

2.4   Parameters to Be Determined

We see from equation (2-27) that at low energies only two parameters may be determined by measuring the scattering cross section as a function of energy, r_0 the effective range of the interaction, and a the scattering length. Since we know, however, that the scattering is spin dependent, we can have different parameters for singlet scattering (a_s and r_{0s}) and for triplet scattering (a_t and r_{0t}). The deuteron ground state being a triplet, gives information only about the triplet interaction.

The analysis can be extended to include noncentral forces and the D state of the deuteron. The same conclusion holds,—namely that only a and r_0 can be determined—but ρ and r_0 now have slightly different definitions in terms of the deuteron D state radial wavefunction w, defined later [equation (2-55)]

$$\rho(-\epsilon, -\epsilon) = 2 \int_0^\infty [e^{-2\gamma r} - (u^2 + w^2)] dr \quad (2\text{-}33)$$

For evaluation of detailed numbers it is convenient to go to one higher approximation, and express the differences between $\rho(-\epsilon, -\epsilon)$ and $\rho(0, -\epsilon)$ etc. It can be shown that

$$k \cot \delta = -1/a + \tfrac{1}{2}k^2 r_0 + P r_0{}^3 k^4 + Q r_0{}^5 k^6 + \cdots \quad (2\text{-}34)$$

where P and Q are shape dependent parameters. So far low-energy experiments alone have not deduced the value of P and Q unequivocally. By using one-pion exchange and other information from high-energy data P and Q may be determined. It is found that P is small and Q almost cancels its effect at 20 mev. The simple formula (2-25) is better than would be expected (Noyes, 1959).

Proton-proton scattering is more complicated to analyze because of the Coulomb field. The scattering from the Coulomb field alone may be solved exactly. The nuclear phase shifts are defined as those phase shifts which, when added to the Coulomb phase shifts, give the observed scattering.

An effective range theory is again applicable and only a_s and r_{0s} may be determined at low energies. Note that the triplet S state for proton-proton scattering cannot exist because of Pauli's exclusion principle. We will not here enter into the details of the separation of the Coulomb and nuclear interactions but will refer to standard works on the subject (Blatt, 1950).

2.5　Experiments at Low Energies

The theory of the effective range thus shows that there is a limited amount of information to be gained by low-energy experiments. To wit: the strength and effective range of the n-p interaction for triplet and singlet states (four parameters) and for the p-p interaction in the triplet state (two parameters). The p-p system cannot occur in the triplet state at low energies. The experiments which, to date, best determine these parameters will now be described.

2.6 Binding Energy of the Deuteron

Since the deuteron has spin 1, the binding energy of the deuteron gives the interaction in the triplet state alone. To measure this we measure the γ-ray energy at the photodisintegration threshold. A Van de Graaf accelerator is used to accelerate electrons to several mev and bremsstrahlung radiation is then produced. The neutrons from the photodisintegration of the deuteron [reaction (1-1)] are measured. The yield of neutrons is plotted as a function of the electron energy and is extrapolated to zero to yield the binding energy. Since the theoretical shape of the cross section curve is known, the extrapolation can be made with little uncertainty, though if the detector discriminates against low energy neutrons, too high a value can be obtained. The crux of the experiment comes in the determination of the electron energy. An ordinary voltmeter (high resistance and microammeter) is not accurate enough for measuring the high voltages involved. The energies of the electron beams have been measured by electrostatic or magnetic deflection. Alternatively, the accelerator is calibrated against a "standard" threshold—the $Li^7(p, n)Be^8$—which is determined elsewhere by electrostatic or magnetic deflection. Two measurements have used this method.

Another method is to study the inverse reaction $H^2(n, \gamma)D^2$. For this the work with a crystal spectrometer is to be preferred for it may be made absolute, although in practice the best measurement, that of Knowles (1962) uses annihilation radiation as a standard. The other measurements use Na^{24} or ThC'' sources as standards, which sources are less well known.

A third method involves a cycle including mass spectrometry. The threshold of the $T^3(p, n)He^3$ reaction and hence the Q value 764.4 ± 0.7 kev is measured. Combined with the β-decay energy of T, 18.4 ± 0.6 kev, an n-p mass difference $n - H = 782.5 \pm 0.3$ kev is derived. This must then be combined with a mass spectrometric measurement of the H_2-D doublet to yield the binding energy of the deuteron.

A fourth method involves any other cycle which can add up to form the binding energy. The $C^{14}(p, n)/N^{14}$ threshold for example,

TABLE 2-1   BINDING ENERGY OF THE DEUTERON

Author	$D(\gamma n)H$ threshold	ϵ mev
Mobley (1950)	Li(pn) standard	2.226 ± 0.003
Noyes (1954)	absolute	2.227 ± 0.003
	mean	2.2265 ± 0.002
	$H_1(n\gamma)D_2$ γ measurement	
Bell (1950)	solenoid ThC$''$ standard	2.2300 ± 0.0030
Motz (1959)	solenoid Na^{24} standard	2.2243 ± 0.0010
Kazi (1961)	curved crystal	2.2255 ± 0.0015
Chupp (1961)	curved crystal	2.2246 ± 0.0015
Knowles (1962)	2 crystal annihilation rad. stand	2.22452 ± 0.0002
Monahan (1961)	scintillation Na^{24} standard	2.2190 ± 0.0020
	mean	2.22450 ± 0.0002
Everling (1960) Wapstra (1961)	$H_2 - D = 1.4421 \pm 0.0009$ mass spectrometer	
van Patter (1954)	$n - p$ from $H^3(p, n)$ He^3, $H^3(\beta+)$ 0.7823 ± 0.0007	2.2244 ± 0.0010
Sanders (1956)	$n - p$ from $C^{14}(pn)N^{14}$, $C^{14}(\beta+)$ 0.7826 ± 0.0004	2.2247 ± 0.0010
	mean	2.22455 ± 0.0009
	overall mean	2.22452 ± 0.00020

combined with the $C^{14}\beta^+$ decay end point. The best results are
tabulated in Table 2-1. The agreement is now good and we take as
the weighted mean $\epsilon = 2.22452 \pm 0.00020$ mev including both
nuclear reaction and mass spectrographic data. The error is determined almost entirely by the measurement of Knowles (1962),
though the others are consistent with this.

2.7   The Incoherent Neutron-Proton Scattering Cross Section

The energies needed here are energies sufficiently high that
molecular effects are absent, yet low compared with the binding
energy of the deuteron and the (negative) binding energy of the

virtual singlet state. This range is 1 to 300 ev. The experiment measures an incoherent addition of the singlet and triplet scattering amplitudes

$$\sigma_t = 4\pi a^2 = 4\pi[\tfrac{3}{4}a_t^2 + \tfrac{1}{4}a_s^2] \qquad (2\text{-}35)$$

In the experiment of Melkonian (1949) the neutrons were obtained from a cyclotron, and their energies measured by a velocity analyzer. The cross section is measured by measuring the difference in attenuation of a hydrocarbon absorber and a carbon absorber with the same number of carbon atoms. The possible effect of efficiency with counting rate was eliminated by verifying that the correct counting rate change was observed when a boron lined aperture was inserted.

Additional use may be made of the *coherent* scattering of neutrons by hydrogen gas at low temperature. At low-neutron velocities this gives

$$\sigma = \sigma_{\text{abs}} + 2K_{11}X_{\text{ortho}}(a_t - a_s)^2$$

$$+ K_{00}X_{\text{para}}(3a_t + a_s)^2 + \text{small correction terms} \qquad (2\text{-}36)$$

where σ_{abs} is the np capture cross section (infra), X_{ortho} and X_{para} are the fractions of ortho and parahydrogen K_{11} and K_{00} are given by the theory of the hydrogen molecule and are well known at zero energy. Since, as we shall see, $|a_s|$ is so much larger than a_t, both (2-35) and (2-36) are dominated by a_s provided that the fraction of ortho hydrogen is not small. $X_{\text{ortho}} = 0.75$ at room temperatures.

Unfortunately the measurements are not with zero energy neutrons but at intermediate energies, and are critically dependent on the exact theory of the hydrogen molecule. The calculations of Brimberg (1956), for example, agree exactly for a harmonic oscillator model, but are higher for an anharmonic oscillator. The results are summarized in Table 2-2.

2.8 The Coherent Neutron-Proton Scattering Amplitude

The best measurements of the n-p triplet coherent scattering amplitude have been with a liquid mirror. The principle and

TABLE 2-2 np INCOHERENT SCATTERING

Author	Method	$\sigma_t = \pi[3a_t^2 + a_s^2]$ (barns)
Melkonian (1949)	σ_{np}(1–20 ev)	20.360 ± 0.050 [a]
Squires (1953)	σ_{np}(0.01–0.1 ev)	20.410 ± 0.140
		20.365 ± 0.05
		= 20.365(1 ± 0.0025)

[a] This error is reduced from the published error after discussion with Dr. Melkonian to conform to the modern tendency of quoting a standard error.

method have been more fully described by Hughes (1953) and in the original papers Hughes (1950), Ringo (1951), Dickinson (1962). The idea of the use of mirrors in coherent neutron scattering comes from earlier x-ray work. The refractive index (n) of a crystal for the neutron waves is given by

$$n^2 = 1 - (\lambda^2 Na/\pi) \qquad (2\text{-}37)$$

where λ is the wavelength, N the number of nuclei per unit volume and a the coherent scattering amplitude. For x-rays and neutrons, in contrast to optics, n is less than 1. This leads to the phenomenon of total external reflection. The measurement of a coherent scattering amplitude then is made by measuring the *critical angle* for external reflection of neutrons at a certain wavelength. This critical angle θ is then given by

$$\theta^2 = \lambda^2 Na/\pi \qquad (2\text{-}38)$$

Of course, the mirror may be an interface between two media in which case the coherent amplitudes are directly compared.

Technically, it is a little difficult to measure the reflection from liquid hydrogen. Therefore a hydrocarbon is used, and, the measurement is an algebraic sum of the coherent scattering amplitudes of the neutrons from hydrogen and carbon. Since the amplitudes have the opposite sign, the effect to be measured is amplified, pro-

vided that the carbon amplitude is well known. Figure 2-2 shows
the apparatus used.

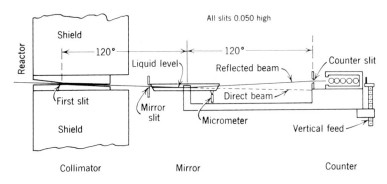

Figure 2-2. Apparatus for neutron reflection from liquids (from Burgy).

It is not convenient to obtain a monochromatic group of neutrons
from the reactor, because of the large reduction of intensity consequent upon this. A method was adopted which avoided use of monochromatic neutrons. This intensity distribution of neutrons decreases sharply with increasing wavelength so the reflected intensity
(which is proportional to the integral from infinite wavelength up to
the critical wavelength) decreases even faster and is a sensitive
function of wavelength.

The experiment therefore consisted of measurements of those
values of the incident angle that give constant intensity (i.e., constant critical wavelength) as the H/C ratio is varied. From equation (2-38) we see that a plot of θ^2 vs. H/C ratio should reach zero
at the point where $a = 0$, and the hydrogen and carbon scatterings
cancel. Figure 2-3 shows such a plot for three different intensities.
The liquids used were triethylbenzene $C_{12}H_{18}$, cyclohexane C_6H_{10},
and a mixture of benzene and cyclohexane to give a H/C ratio of
1.7 ($C_{10}H_{17}$). Passel *et al.*, have repeated the experiment. Hughes
also measured the critical angle by comparison with the angle from

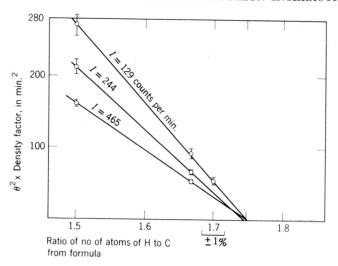

Figure 2-3. Graph for determining the balance point of H to C coherent neutron amplitudes (from Burgy).

beryllium; and Passel *et al.*, have also compared water (H_2O) and dodecane $C_{12}H_{26}$ mirrors. The results are summarized in Table 2-3.

TABLE 2-3   LIQUID MIRROR EXPERIMENTS

Author	Method	a_c/a_H
Hughes (1950)	comparison of θ_{int} to Be	-1.771 ± 0.010
Ringo (1951)	comparison of hydrocarbons	-1.751 ± 0.010 [a,b]
Dickinson (1962)	comparison of hydrocarbons	-1.775 ± 0.004
Dickinson (1962)	comparison of H_2O and dodecane	-1.784 ± 0.010 [c]
	comparison of θ_{int} to Be	-1.765 ± 0.012
	Mean	$1.7718 \pm 0.0031(1 \pm 0.0018)$

[a] The error here has been arbitrarily doubled to allow for the lack of study of systematic errors performed by Dickinson.

[b] The values of Hughes (1950) and Ringo (1951) have been corrected for the neutron-electron interaction following Dickinson (1962).

[c] Assuming $a_0/a_c = 0.878 \pm 0.004$.

The coherent cross section for carbon must also be measured. If carbon had one isotope of spin zero, this could be measured by a total cross section measurement. The "bound atom" cross section is greater than that for a free atom. The coherent amplitude becomes

$$4\pi a_c^{\,2} = \sigma_{coh}\text{ (bound)} = [(A+1)/A]^2\sigma_{tot} \qquad (2\text{-}38a)$$

Correction must be made to this for isotopic incoherence and spin incoherence due to the 1% C^{13} impurity. The coherent scattering on C^{13} has been measured and so has the total cross section (Koehler, 1952). The coherent scattering amplitude is the same sign and almost the same magnitude as for C^{13} so isotopic incoherence is less than 1 in 10^4. The total cross section of C^{13} could be a little larger, leading to a spin incoherent cross section in natural carbon of 0.20 $\pm$ 0.30%. From the total cross section values in Table 2-4

$$a_c = 6.622(1 \pm 0.0025) \times 10^{-13}\text{ cm} \qquad (2\text{-}38b)$$

TABLE 2-4   NEUTRON CARBON CROSS SECTION

Author	σ_{tot} (barns)
Havens (1949)	4.700 ± 0.050
Wollan (1962)	4.670 ± 0.030
Sailor (1962)	4.739 ± 0.029
Brugger (1956)	4.690 ± 0.100
	4.704 ± 0.019
	$= 4.704(1 \pm 0.004)$

Then the coherent scattering cross section for hydrogen becomes from (2-38b) and Table 2-3

$$f = 2[\tfrac{3}{4}a_t + \tfrac{1}{4}a_s]$$
$$= (-3.737 \pm 0.011) \times 10^{-13}\text{ cm } (1 \pm 0.0031) \qquad (2\text{-}39)$$

Another method is available for measuring $f = \tfrac{2}{4}[3a_t + a_s]$: the scattering of slow neutrons by pure parahydrogen. Again a total cross section is measured as a function of the neutron energy—the energy measured by time of flight. Now, it is not possible to work at low enough neutron energies that the theory of the hydrogen molecule may be neglected. The cross section is expressable at low temperatures and low-neutron energies in the form (2-36).

$X_{para} = 0.9979$ and $X_{ortho} = 0.0021$ are the fractions of para and ortho hydrogen at the temperature (20.4°K) concerned. K_{∞} and K_{11} come from the theory of the hydrogen molecule. The corrections from the first and third terms are about 2% of the total.

The best experiment has been performed by Squires (1955), who finds a value

$$f = \tfrac{2}{4}[3a_t + a_s] = -3.800 \pm 0.050 \times 10^{-13} \text{ cm} \quad (2\text{-}41)$$

This result could be changed by a reevaluation of the theory of the hydrogen molecule.

Another, less accurate, result, is obtainable from coherent scattering by crystals. The data on f are summarized in Table 2-5; the

TABLE 2-5   COHERENT NEUTRON-PROTON AMPLITUDE

Author	Method	$f \times 10^{13}$ cm
Tables 2-3 and 2-4	Liquid mirror	-3.737 ± 0.011
Squires (1955)	Parahydrogen	-3.800 ± 0.050
Shull (1948)	Crystal (NaH)	-3.900 ± 0.100
	Mean	-3.741 ± 0.011
		$= -3.741(1 \pm 0.0031)$

error in the mean is primarily that of the liquid mirror measurements, though the others affect slightly the value of the mean.

2.9   Neutron-Proton Scattering at Moderate Energies

In order to measure the singlet effective range the singlet amplitude must be measured at a second energy. A measurement of the

np scattering total cross section around 400 kev accomplishes this. Such a cross section is dominated mainly by triplet scattering, so a precise measurement is needed as well as a knowledge of the triplet parameters. The apparatus used by Fields (1954) is shown in Figure 2-4.

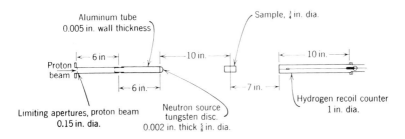

Figure 2-4. Experimental arrangement for 1 mev and 2.5 mev np total cross section (from Fields).

The best measurements are those of Engelke (1962). Neutrons from the $Li^7(p, n)Be^7$ reaction have an energy given by the kinematics of the reaction and the particle energy. They are detected by the $N^{14}(n, p)C^{14}$ reaction in a gaseous scintillator. The neutrons are produced in a thin target and the energy of the accelerator is adjusted for maximum counting rate. Under these circumstances the energy of source and detector are well defined.

The transmission is measured through a pure hydrocarbon (heptane). Careful measurements are made of multiple scattering in the target, room scattering, detection of γ-ray background, variations of efficiency with count rate, sample purity, and the energy of the incident neutrons.

Earlier measurements used detectors which are also sensitive to lower energy neutrons, thus rendering corrections more important. Table 2-6 summarizes the available data.

TABLE 2-6   MEDIUM ENERGY np CROSS SECTIONS

Author	Reaction	Neutron energy (mev)	Total np cross section (barns)
Engelke (1962)	$N^{14}(n, p)C^{14}$	0.4926	6.202 ± 0.011
Engelke (1962)	$Ne^{20}(n, \alpha)$ detector	3.205	2.206 ± 0.007
Fields (1954)	$p(Li^7, Be^7)n$	1.005	4.228 ± 0.018
Storrs (1954)	$p(Li^7, Be^7)n$	5.315	3.675 ± 0.016
Fields (1954)	$d(d, He_3)n$	2.540	2.525 ± 0.009
Hafner (1953)	$d(d, He_3)n$	4.749	1.690 ± 0.007
Poss (1952)	$d(T, \alpha)n$	14.100 ± 0.050	0.689 ± 0.005

At energies of about 400 kev, the data are sensitive to the low-energy triplet amplitude and to the low-energy singlet amplitudes. At 17 mev, the np triplet phase is near 90° (Figure 7-1) given by $k \cot \delta = 0$. Then the triplet cross section is given only by the

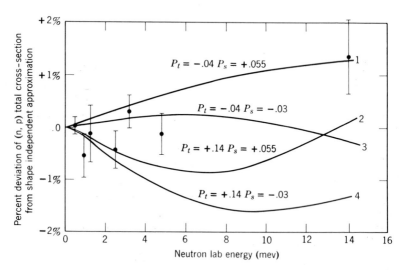

Figure 2-5. Plot of deviation of np cross section from shape independent approximation versus energy for various shape parameters P; Q is assumed zero. The data of Table 2-6 are shown. Parameters r_t, a_t, a_s, r_s are as tabulated here.

energy and the total cross section can give the singlet shape parameter, somewhat independent of the zero energy parameters.

The 400 kev data give a singlet effective range of (2.46 ± 0.12)
$\times 10^{-13}$ cm when analyzed together with the low-energy parameters. The five earlier measurements give $r_s = 2.64 \pm 0.12 \times 10^{-13}$
cm (Noyes 1963). This difference may be systematic. We assume
henceforth a value of $(2.51 \pm 0.1) \times 10^{-13}$ cm. Assuming this, the
results of the medium energy experiments are plotted in Figure 2-5
assuming the shape independent approximation ($P_s = P_t = 0$) and
for various shape parameters. It should be repeated, however, that
theoretically P_s and P_t are small and the neglected parameters Q_s
and Q_t are not. This is discussed in detail by Noyes (1963).

2.10   Photodisintegration of the Deuteron at
Medium Energies

From the theory we note that the photodisintegration reaction
depends upon the matrix element

$$\int \psi_g ez \psi_f dr \qquad (2\text{-}40)$$

for the electric dipole transition, which is predominant at energies
far from threshold. ψ_f is the wavefunction in the ^3P state of the
neutron-proton system, which may be taken equal to the free wavefunction for low energies such that kr is small compared with unity.
This is applicable to quite high values of kr since the average ^3P
interaction is not very large. The initial state ψ_g is the ground
state of the deuteron which is primarily the ^3S state. This wavefunction depends upon the nuclear forces between the neutron and
proton in almost the same way as the neutron-proton scattering
does; the normalization terms have already been discussed. We assume because of the r^2 in the matrix element (2-40) that the contribution from inside the range of nuclear forces is small. It is called
an "outside" integral. This is true for "reasonable" force shapes—
in particular those which have a tail given by one pion exchange.
We may, if we wish, regard the experimental agreement that we
will obtain as a proof of the reasonableness of the force shape.

The square of the normalizing factor $N_g{}^2 = 2\gamma/(1 - \gamma\rho)$ there-fore appears directly in the expression for the cross section. A measurement of the cross section to 1% can yield a measurement of ρ to 2%. The method used has been to use a calibrated γ-ray source, at a known distance from an ionization chamber counter filled with deuterium gas. The protons from the disintegration are thus counted directly.

The source calibrations differ in each case. The 2.615 γ ray occurs in every β decay of ThC''. The α source was calibrated by measur-ing the α particles from the parent. This was done with a weaker source which was later compared with the strong source used for the photodisintegration.

The 2.753 γ ray occurs in almost every β decay of Na^{24}. A source was then calibrated by $\beta\gamma$ coincidences and again compared with the stronger source used in the deuteron measurement.

The 6.14 mev γ ray from an excited O^{16} nucleus, is produced by the reaction $F^{19}(p, \alpha)O^{16}$. A counter was calibrated by $\alpha\gamma$ coinci-dences and then used as the monitor in the deuteron measurements. The same counter was calculated to have an efficiency proportional to energy and used at several other gamma-ray energies. These three source calibrations were the major sources of uncertainty in the experiments.

At the low energies the total cross section is given not only by the electric dipole disintegration but also by the magnetic dipole $^3S \rightarrow {}^1S$ transition. The energy dependence of this is quite well known and the neutron proton capture cross section (about to be described) measures the inverse process at zero energy very pre-cisely, so this effect can be subtracted to yield the electric dipole cross section. The effective ranges so deduced are tabulated in Table 2-7. The experiments are well discussed by Bishop (1950) but the exact values should be taken from Table 2-7.

As said before, these results cannot be directly compared with the results from the experiments 1 and 2 because of the shape de-pendence of the effective range, which can make a 3% difference with our present uncertainties.

These measurements could probably be improved by a factor of

TABLE 2-7   CROSS SECTION FOR PHOTODISINTEGRATION
OF THE DEUTERON

Author	γ-ray energy	Cross section millibarns	Effective range $[\rho(-\epsilon, -\epsilon)]$
Marin (1953) (1954)	2.615	13.00 $\pm$ 0.28	1.92 $\pm$ 0.08
McMurray (1955)	2.753	15.00 $\pm$ 0.60	1.74 $\pm$ 0.10
Barnes (1952)	6.14	21.9 $\pm$ 1.0	
	and		1.77 $\pm$ 0.09
Wilkinson [a] (1952)	4.45– 17.6	various	
		Mean	1.82 $\pm$ 0.05 $\times$ 10^{-13} cm

[a] The number is corrected downward from that quoted in the reference to allow for contributions to the 17.6 mev data from other multipoles as discussed further in Chapter 8.

3 with modern techniques, though they are sensitive to the difference between the energy of the γ ray and the binding energy of the deuteron.

2.11   The Neutron-Proton Capture Cross Section

The neutron proton capture cross section is 100 times less than the scattering cross section so it cannot be measured in a transmission measurement.

There are three main types of measurement to measure σ_{cap}. The first measures the mean lifetime of neutrons in a hydrogenous medius with no other capturing elements. The lifetime is related to the capture cross section by the relation.

$$4\sigma_{cap}\tau v n = 1 \qquad (2\text{-}41)$$

where v is the velocity of the neutrons, n is the number of hydrogen atoms per unit volume in the material. Now we know that $v\sigma_{cap}$ is constant for energies below about 50 kev. Thus if fast neutrons are slowed down in water the absorption will become exponential in time after the first few collisions—that is after 5 μsec. The experiments then require a pulsed neutron source, a large (essentially infinite) tank of water, a neutron detector and a time sorter.

The two most precise measurements are those of Meads (1956) and von Dardel (1954). In both of these the neutrons were produced from a d-d reaction, where the deuteron beam was pulsed. Various systematic errors must be carefully avoided. The water tank must be large enough that corrections for its size are easy, and can be made experimentally and not only theoretically. The unavoidable entry of the deuteron beam tube into the tank introduces an error. Meads used a large tank and his counter matched the moderator by detecting neutron capture gamma rays; von Dardel used a smaller tank, with BF_3 detectors, and a more complicated calculation for the capture cross section.

The second type of experiment has been performed by Hammermesh (1953) following the lines of the early experiments of Fermi. A neutron source is placed at the center of a tank of water sufficiently large that essentially all the neutrons are slowed down and captured by the hydrogen nuclei. A quantity of sodium iodide is added, sufficiently small that most of the neutrons are captured by the hydrogen yet sufficiently large that the activity induced in the iodine is measurable. After equilibrium has been established, the neutron source is removed, the solution thoroughly stirred, and the iodine activity of an aliquot fraction is measured. Since the oxygen and sodium atoms have small capture cross sections, the iodine activity is given by

$$A_1 = K \frac{N_I \sigma_I}{N_I \sigma_I + N_H \sigma_H} \qquad (2\text{-}42)$$

where K would be the activity if all the neutrons were captured by the iodine, N_I, N_H are the number of iodine and hydrogen atoms per cm^3 of solution and σ_I, σ_H are the capture cross sections for hydrogen and iodine.

This procedure is now repeated with a small quantity of borax (essentially boron) added. The activity is now given by

$$A_2 = K \frac{N_I \sigma_I}{N_I \sigma_I + N_H \sigma_H + N_B \sigma_B} \qquad (2\text{-}43)$$

The ratio

$$R = \frac{A_I}{A_2} \frac{N_B \sigma_B + N_I \sigma_I + N_H \sigma_H}{N_I \sigma_I + N_H \sigma_H} \tag{2-44}$$

or

$$R - 1 = \frac{\sigma_B}{\sigma_H} \frac{N_B}{N_H} \left(1 + \frac{N_I}{N_H} \frac{\sigma_I}{\sigma_H} \right)^{-1} \tag{2-45}$$

The second term in the bracket can be made as small as is compatible with the available intensity, and σ_I does not therefore have to be known well. Thus σ_H / σ_B is determined accurately.

A similar experiment has been briefly reported (Baker, 1958) where the detector was a boron loaded emulsion detecting by the $^{10}B(n, \sigma)^7 L$ reaction.

The cross sections for hydrogen and boron may also be compared by a pile oscillator technique (Harris, 1953).

The boron cross section measured by a transmission experiment has been a source of trouble. It is important to measure relative to a boron sample of known isotopic constitution since the $^{10}B/^{11}B$ ratio varies in natural boron. Thus one cannot directly compare the quantities σ_B / σ_H in different laboratories.

Another indirect method of lifetime measurement, is to measure directly the diffusion constant D for slow neutrons in water and the diffusion length L of slow neutrons in water. The lifetime of neutrons in water is given by $\tau = L^2/D$. This comparison is already indirectly made by Meads in comparing experimental and theoretical corrections to his lifetime measurement. The equipment used by Meads (1956) is shown in Figure 2-6. Other data may be combined to yield a value of the cross section.

We feel that a further separation of these experiments into separate groups as far as experimental methods is concerned, is no more meaningful than the comparison of the experiments themselves. A least squares analysis taking account of all the inner correlations is needed to get the most out of the data. No one has done this and in Table 2-8 is summarized the major data and an ordinary mean is shown. It is clear that the data are consistent.

In the exact analysis of these experiments the shape parameter

effective range theory has to be included. We note, however, that
if we wish to measure the shape parameters P and Q in (2-34), then
it is preferable to consider the high-energy experiments discussed
in subsequent chapters. We can compute, for example, the values
of P from the one pion exchange potential introduced in Chapter 7
to relate high-energy experiments. Glendenning (1962) has thus

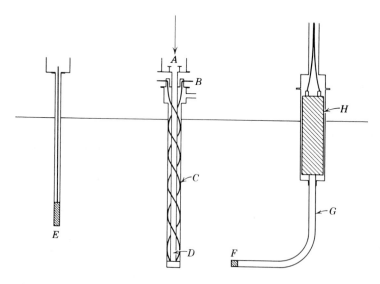

Figure 2-6. Equipment for measuring the lifetime of neutrons in water (from
Meads): A, diaphragm to define the deuteron beam; B, liquid air inlet; C,
vacuum jacket; D, heavy ice target; E, BF$_3$ neutron monitor; F, scintillator;
G, light guide; H, photomultiplier.

calculated $P_t = +0.017 \pm 0.013$ where the error comes from errors
in other np parameters.

We may then summarize the parameters of the low-energy np
system; experiments measure the binding energy of the deuteron ϵ;
the incoherent np scattering cross section, the np coherent scattering amplitude, f, whence we may deduce γ, a_t, a_s, $\rho(0, -\epsilon)$. From

the experiments on medium energy np scattering we deduce the singlet effective range. From the low-energy photodisintegration of the deuteron we have $\rho(-\epsilon, -\epsilon)$ and hence can measure P_t to compare with the theoretical value. The experimental value of P_t is larger than theoretical but is of low precision.

This comparison of P_t with the one pion exchange value may be regarded as a confirmation of the general approach. Thus the computation of $\rho(-\epsilon, -\epsilon)$ in Table 2-7 and Table 2-10 from the photodisintegration of the deuteron is dependent on the assumption that the integral in the matrix element (2-40) is an "outside" integral—that is to say that it has no components from inside the range of nuclear forces. Because of the r^2 term this is not unreasonable, but nucleon-nucleon potentials can be invented for which this is not true. Fortunately the meson-theoretic potential is not one of these. The experimental agreement would be improved if we omit the photodisintegration measurement with 2.615 mev γ rays.

We note that the error on a_t and a_s is determined now primarily by the error in experiments on the total cross sections of hydrogen, carbon 12 and carbon 13 at low energies are "easy" experiments. The fractional error in $\rho(0, -\epsilon)$ is five times the error in a_t. But the error in $\rho(-\epsilon, -\epsilon)$ is only twice the error in the photodisintegration cross section, suggesting a remeasurement of this quantity.

The analysis of the np capture cross section follows the procedure of Austern (1953, 1960). The capture cross section is given by the formula

$$\sigma_c = \frac{Q \left[\int u_g u_s dr \right]^2}{1 - \gamma \rho(-\epsilon, -\epsilon)} \tag{2-46}$$

where

$$Q = \frac{\pi}{2k} \frac{e^2}{M_c^2} \left(\frac{\epsilon}{\hbar c} \right)^3 (\mu_n - \mu_p)^2 2\gamma (a_s)^2$$

$$= 1150 \pm 5 \tag{2-47}$$

where we have inserted for the wave number k that for 2,200 m/sec neutrons to which the measurements are referred. The error is primarily due to a_s.

$$\int u_g u_s dr = |m_0| - \tfrac{1}{4}[\rho_s + \rho_t(-\epsilon, -\epsilon)] - \tfrac{1}{2}(P_D/N_g{}^2) + C \quad (2\text{-}48)$$

where m_0 is the zero range value $5.098 \pm 0.025 \times 10^{-13}\,\mathrm{cm}^{-1}$, P_D is the deuteron D state probability and C is a small (1%) shape dependent constant.

For this analysis we derive $\rho_t(-\epsilon, -\epsilon)$ from $\rho_t(0, -\epsilon)$ using the theoretical value of P_t (not that experimentally derived) to obtain

$$\sigma_c = 0.3109 \pm 0.005$$
$$= 0.3109(1 \pm 0.018) \text{ barns at 2,200 m/sec} \quad (2\text{-}49)$$

which is lower than the experimental value in Table 2-8 by $0.020 \pm$

TABLE 2-8 np CAPTURE CROSS SECTION EXPERIMENTS

Author	Method	np capture cross section (barns)
von Dardel (1954)	Lifetime, corrections theoretical	0.333 ± 0.003
Meads (1956)	Lifetime, corrections theoretical and experimental	0.335 ± 0.004
Baker (1958)	Ratio to boron by integrating tank	0.327 ± 0.004
Hamermesh (1953)	Ratio to boron by integrating tank	0.329 ± 0.004
Harris (1953)	Ratio to boron by pile oscillator	0.332 ± 0.007
Baker (1958)	Measurement of D and L	0.329 ± 0.005
		0.3314 ± 0.0019

0.007 barns or $6 \pm 2\%$. This difference is *larger* than a value calculated using meson theory by Sugawara (1955, 1960) but is the same order as a similar discrepancy in the addition of neutron and proton momenta to form the deuteron magnetic moment and its interpretation in terms of the D state probability (see infra).

2.12   Proton-Proton Scattering at 400 kev

The p-p scattering at any one (low) energy can tell one and only one parameter: the $^1S_0$ phase shift. In order to measure the two parameters that are possible at low energies, the $^1S_0$ phase must be measured at two different energies, obviously as widely separated as possible. The first measurement we choose was performed by Cooper (1954).

Pure Coulomb scattering or protons by protons will result in an

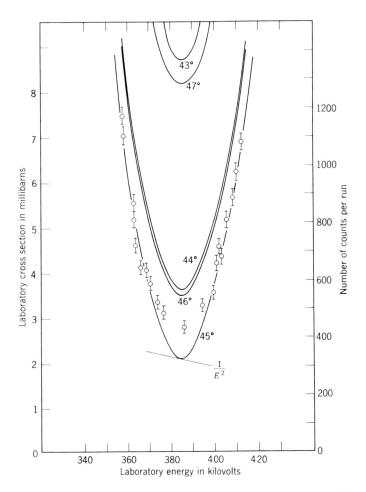

Figure 2-7. Detailed *p-p* cross section at laboratory angles near 45° with experimental points of Cooper.

angular distribution $1/\theta^4$ for small θ, as given by the Rutherford scattering law. The antisymmetrization introduced by Mott to take account of the Pauli principle leads of course to a symmetry about $\theta = \pi/2$. Pure nuclear scattering in the $^1S_0$ state leads to isotropic scattering in the center of mass. Since the Coulomb force is repulsive and the nuclear force is attractive, there will be an interference at some angle, leading to a very low cross section. This angle will vary with energy and with the $^1S_0$ phase.

The beam of protons from a Van de Graaf accelerator passed through narrow canals onto a target of especially pure gaseous hydrogen at 1.5 cm pressure. Protons scattered at 45° lab ($\pi/2$ cm) were detected in a proportional counter. The protons were collected and monitored by a current integrator.

The cross section was calculated and plotted as a function of energy (Fig. 2-7). On this same plot are the calculated interference minima for a curve of nuclear phase shift vs. energy taken from previous data. At this minimum the nuclear phase shift is approximately equal to $e^2/\hbar v$, where v is the relative velocity of the two protons at the energy of the minimum. The energy was determined to be 383 ± 1.5 kev, i.e., to 0.4% in v^2 and therefore the phase shift is known to about 0.2%. With this method of data taking, only the energy need be determined absolutely. The other parameters—solid angle, counter efficiency—only enter as correction terms. This experiment is being repeated at Los Alamos.

2.13 Proton–Proton Scattering at 1 to 3 mev

There are now precise measurements from Wisconsin (Knecht, 1959) available. No trick is possible as for the lower energy measurement to avoid systematic errors. The apparatus is shown in Figure 2-8. The incident beam with an energy spread of 0.1% is collimated by a long tube containing the defining apertures A_1, A_2, and A_3. Without passing through foils, the beam enters the scattering volume. The unscattered beam is collected and monitored by a Faraday cup which allows absolute measurement of beam intensity. The scattered protons pass through two defining slits onto a proportional counter. The detection solid angle is defined by the

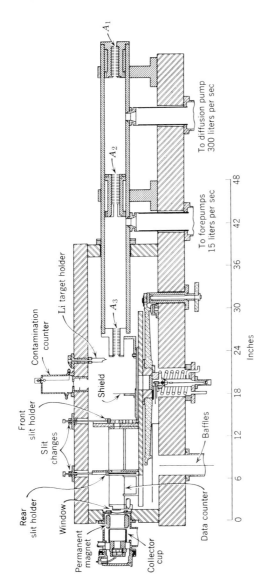

Figure 2-8. Sectional view of *p-p* scattering apparatus used at Wisconsin with scattering angle set to zero (from Knecht).

slits and the effective target length is defined also by the slits and varies as sin θ, where θ is the angle of scattering.

We can express the cross section σ in the form

$$\sigma = \gamma \sin \theta / nNG \qquad (2\text{-}50)$$

where γ is the yield of scattered particles per n incident particles; N is the target proton density, and G is the geometrical factor. Small sources of error which needed correction include, counter inefficiency, counting rate corrections, slit edge scattering, double nuclear scattering, contamination, incorrect averaging over the finite geometry. The energy was determined in terms of the $\text{Li}^7(p, n)\text{Be}^7$ threshold to 0.09%. Measurements were made at 13 angles from 12°–90° cm at 1.855 mev, 11 angles from 12° cm to 70° cm at 1.397 mev, 14 angles from 12° cm to 100° cm at 2.425 mev with precisions varying from 0.11% at large angles to 0.3% at small angles.

For the p-p system the effective range theory must be modified to take account of Coulomb forces and the identity of the two particles. This can be done, and the modification must include a vacuum polarization contribution. The calculations are too complex to include here (Jackson, 1950, Foldy, 1955, deWit, 1958, Durand, 1957, Heller, 1960), but we state the results. The cross section is given by the symmetrized amplitude.

$$\begin{aligned}
|f^s(\theta)|^2 = {} & |f_c{}^s(\theta)|^2 + (4/k^2) \sin^2 \delta_0 \\
& + (4/k) \ \text{Re} \ \{f_c{}^s(\theta)[e^{2i\tau_0} \exp{(i\delta_0)} \sin \delta_0]^*\} \\
& + 2 \ \text{Re} \ \{f_{vp}{}^s(\theta)[f_c{}^s(\theta) + (2/k) \exp{(i\delta_0)} \sin \delta_0]^*\} \\
& + (4/k) \left\{ \left[\sum_{L=2,4} (2L+1) \right] e^{2i(\sigma_L - \sigma_0)} \delta_L P_L[f_c{}^s(\theta) \right. \\
& \hspace{3cm} \left. + (2/k) \exp{(i\delta_0)} \sin \delta_0]^* \right\} \quad (2\text{-}51)
\end{aligned}$$

where the subscripts c and vp on the amplitudes denote ordinary Coulomb and vacuum polarization, respectively, the superscript s denotes the singlet state, δ_0 is the "nuclear" phase shift for $L = 0$, τ_L and σ_L are the vacuum polarization and Coulomb phases for angular momentum L.

LOW-ENERGY THEORY AND EXPERIMENT

The effective range expansion becomes

$$\frac{C^2 k}{1 - \phi_0}\left[(1 + X_0)\cot\delta_0 - \tan\tau_0\right] + \frac{h(n)}{R} + \frac{l_0(n)}{R}$$
$$= -1/a + \tfrac{1}{2}k^2 r_0 \quad (2\text{-}52)$$

Noyes (1963) has analyzed the data to yield values of δ_0 and hence a, r_0. For this analysis it is important to verify that the addition of small P wave phase shifts, up to the amount allowed by the data does not change the deduced value of δ_0. The results are in Table 2-9, and a and r_0 are shown in Table 2-10.

TABLE 2-9   LOW ENERGY p-p SCATTERING

E mev	δ_0
0.3829	$14.582 \pm 0.086°$
1.399	$39.299 \pm 0.020°$
1.855	$44.342 \pm 0.020°$
2.425	$48.381 \pm 0.020°$
3.035	$51.038 \pm 0.020°$

TABLE 2-10   PARAMETERS OF THE LOW ENERGY
NUCLEON-NUCLEON SCATTERING

Table 2-1	$\epsilon = 2.22452(1 \pm 0.00009)$ mev
Derived	$\gamma = 0.231688(1 \pm 0.00005) \times 10^{-13}$ cm
Table 2-2	$\sigma_0 = 20.365(1 \pm 0.0025) \times 10^{-24}$ cm^2
Table 2-5	$f = -3.741(1 \pm 0.0031) \times 10^{-13}$ cm
Derived	$a_t = 5.399(1 \pm 0.0018) \times 10^{-13}$ cm
	$= (5.399 \pm 0.011) \times 10^{-13}$ cm
Derived	$a_s = -23.680(1 \pm 0.0012) \times 10^{-13}$ cm
	$= (-23.680 \pm 0.028) \times 10^{-13}$ cm
Derived	$\rho(0, -\epsilon) = 1.732(1 \pm 0.007) \times 10^{-13}$ cm
	$= (1.732 \pm 0.012) \times 10^{-13}$ cm
Table 2-6	$r_{os} = \rho_s(0, 0) = (2.46 \pm 0.12) \times 10^{-13}$ cm
Table 2-7	$\rho(-\epsilon, -\epsilon) = (1.82 \pm 0.05) \times 10^{-13}$ cm
Derived	$P_t = +0.15 \pm 0.09$
Table 2-9	$a_{pp} = -7.778(1 \pm 0.0011) \times 10^{-13}$ cm
Table 2-9	$r_{opp} = 2.714(1 \pm 0.004) \times 10^{-13}$ cm

The well known comparison of the a_s for np scattering and a for p-p scattering shows that there is a difference. Since a_s is large, a small inequality in potential depth can lead to large changes. The existing numbers are consistent with a $1\frac{1}{2}\%$ difference in well depth. For most purposes, this difference is zero. There seems also to be no difference in effective range between np and pp singlet states. This leads to the assumption of charge independence assumed in most of this book and discussed in Chapter 9.

2.14   Quadrupole Moment of the Deuteron

We include here the measurement by molecular beam techniques, of the quadrupole moment of the deuteron (Kolsky, 1952, Auffray, 1961). The quadrupole moment is defined as

$$Q = \int (3z^2 - r^2)\rho dr \qquad (2\text{-}53)$$

This measured by the radiofrequency spectrum of deuterium.

Experiments measure very precisely eQq, where q is the gradient of the electric field along the molecular axis at one deuteron. q must be calculated. The wavefunctions used for this calculation give nearly the correct molecular binding energy. The value deduced is

$$Q = 2.82 \times 10^{-27} \text{ cm}^2 \qquad (2\text{-}54)$$

The quadrupole moment is related to the probability of finding the deuteron in a D state. In order to see this, we abridge a discussion in Blatt (1952). We write the wavefunctions for S and D states,

$$\psi = \psi_S + \psi_D \qquad \psi_S = \frac{u(r)}{r\sqrt{4\pi}} N_g \qquad \psi_D = N_g \frac{w(r)}{r\sqrt{4\pi}} \mathcal{Y}_{121} \qquad (2\text{-}55)$$

the S state probability becomes

$$N_g \int_0^\infty u^2(r)dr = 1 - P_D \qquad (2\text{-}56)$$

and the D state probability

$$N_g \int_0^\infty w^2(r)dr = P_D \qquad (2\text{-}57)$$

and $N_g \int_0^\infty [u^2(r) + w^2(r)]dr = 1$ is the normalization. The quadrupole moment then becomes, using (2-53) and (2-55)

$$Q = (\tfrac{1}{50})^{1/2} N_g{}^2 \int_0^\infty r^2 uw\,dr - \tfrac{1}{20} N_g{}^2 \int_0^\infty r^2 w^2 dr \qquad (2\text{-}58)$$

Since $w \ll u$, we take the first term

$$Q = (\tfrac{1}{50})^{1/2} N_g{}^2 \int_0^\infty r^2 uw\,dr \qquad (2\text{-}59)$$

Because of the factor r^2 in the integrand, the main contribution comes from outside the range of the forces. The normalization at large distances is taken

$$(u^2 + w^2) \rightarrow e^{-2\gamma r} \text{ as } (r \rightarrow \infty) \qquad (2\text{-}60)$$

Assuming the integral (2-59) is given entirely by the value outside the range of forces, we get

$$Q = \frac{1}{\sqrt{8}} \frac{2\gamma}{R} N_w \frac{1}{\gamma^3} \qquad (2\text{-}61)$$

where R is the ratio of the asymptotic wavefunctions for the D and S states. Thus

$$R = \sqrt{2}\, Q\gamma^2 \qquad (2\text{-}62)$$

showing that the D state wavefunctions outside the range of forces is given primarily by the quadrupole moment. The fraction of D state P_D is not so determined.

However, the one pion exchange for np forces (see Chapters 3 and 7) gives, by itself, a value for Q of 2.88×10^{-27} cm^2 (Glendenning, 1962) which is almost the experimental value; so if we believe that one pion exchange contributes significantly to the np system, then we find that the part of the D state wavefunction w inside the range of nuclear forces is also well determined. The D state probability then becomes

$$P_D = \int w^2 dr \bigg/ \int (u^2 + w^2) dr = (6.5 \pm 1)\% \qquad (2\text{-}63)$$

This conclusion is at variance with older assumptions of 3–4%. The 6.5% value is given by the potentials discussed in Chapter 7; by the requirement to fit the photodisintegration of the deuteron in Chapter 8; and by coherent production of π mesons from the deuteron (Hadjioannou, 1962).

2.15   Magnetic Moment of the Deuteron

The magnetic moments of the neutron, proton, and deuteron have been measured by nuclear resonance and atomic beam techniques (Sommer, 1951, Bloch, 1948, and Wimmett, 1953). It is found that the magnetic moment of the deuteron is not quite the sum of those of the neutron and proton. If we could neglect relativistic and meson exchange effects we could write

$$\tfrac{3}{2}(\mu_n + \mu_p - \tfrac{1}{2})P_D = \mu_n + \mu_p - \mu_d \qquad (2\text{-}64)$$

where P_D is the probability of the d state of the deuteron.

The experimental numbers are:

$$\mu_p = 2.792680 \pm 0.000011$$

$$\mu_n = 1.91304 \pm 0.00010$$

$$\mu_d = 0.85741 \pm 0.00008$$

whence P_D is 4%.

The value of 4% disagrees with the value $(6.5 \pm 1)\%$ deduced from the quadrupole moment and one pion exchange. However, there are relativistic and meson exchange current corrections to the electric and magnetic moments which may be a few percent and of either sign. A 2% correction to Q clearly makes no appreciable difference, but a 2% correction to μ_n or μ_p can change P_D by $\pm 2\%$—a big correction. Thus it is not possible to use the precise information on magnetic moments until a theory is available.

If a spin-orbit interaction exists in the nucleon-nucleon potential, it will tend to *depress* the value of P_D found from the magnetic moment nonadditivity. Other velocity dependent terms tend to increase it. The present situation is confused (Sugawara, 1950, 1955).

2.16 Hyperfine Structure of the Deuterium Atom

The ratio of the hyperfine structure constants of the hydrogen and deuterium atoms have been measured precisely (Anderson, 1960). The results may be put in the form

$$\frac{\nu_H}{\nu_D} = \frac{4}{3}\frac{\mu_p}{\mu_D}\left(\frac{M_H}{M_D}\right)^3(1-\Delta) \qquad (2\text{-}65)$$

The defect $\Delta = (170.3 \pm 0.5) \times 10^{-6}$. Only a part of this is due to deuteron structure. This part equals $(163 \pm 42) \times 10^{-6}$. It has been pointed out (Sessler, 1958) that this is a distinct datum from the magnetic moment and it is very sensitive to the possible presence of a spin-orbit coupling. At present no good agreement has been achieved. Indications are that if there is a spin orbit force in triplet even states of the np system, a larger $(>7\%)D$ state probability is required.

Chapter 3

The Variety of High-Energy Experiments

3.1 General

Once it is realized that the forces between two nucleons are spin dependent, many more experiments are found to be necessary to determine the interaction. With no spin dependence, it is possible with scattering experiments to measure only one number at each energy and angle—the differential cross section $\sigma(\theta)$. At first sight it appears that there is here a discrepancy, for a theoretical description uses two parameters, the real and imaginary parts of the scattering amplitude. A relation exists, however, between the two. In the forward direction

$$\mathrm{Im}\, f(0) = \frac{k}{4\pi}\, \sigma_{\mathrm{tot}} = \frac{k}{4\pi} \int \frac{d\sigma}{d\Omega} d\Omega$$

$$= \frac{k}{4\pi} \int \sigma(\theta) d\Omega \qquad (3\text{-}1)$$

if the energy is low enough that absorptive (meson producing) processes are absent. This represents the fact that any removal of particles from the incident beam of momentum k must produce a diffraction scattering; it may thus be regarded as a consequence of a particle conservation law. Since the size of the interaction region is not specified by the total cross section, only the forward scattering can be derived. This can be extended to

$$\frac{4\pi}{k} \operatorname{Im} f(\mathbf{k}, \mathbf{k}') = \int f^*(\mathbf{k}, \mathbf{k}'')f(\mathbf{k}'', \mathbf{k})d\mathbf{k}'' \qquad (3\text{-}2)$$

where $f(\mathbf{k}, \mathbf{k}')$ is the amplitude for scattering from a direction $\mathbf{k}$ to $\mathbf{k}'$. If the cross section $f^*(\mathbf{k}, \mathbf{k}')f(\mathbf{k}, \mathbf{k}')$, is measured at all angles, (all $\mathbf{k}$, $\mathbf{k}'$) equation (3-2) enables the real and imaginary parts to be separately determined, by solving the integral equation. It is interesting to note that the phase shift expansion (2-10) is explicitly constructed to satisfy unitarity and hence equation (3-2).

With spin dependence the scattering cross section can depend upon the polarization of the incident particle and the polarization of the struck particle. The polarization of either the incident or the struck particle can be measured, or the correlation between the directions of polarization of the two particles. Since the particles can be polarized in three directions, one along and two perpendicular to the direction of motion, this gives many possibilities. These are shown in the Table 3-1. The usual symbols for the experiments are shown, together with the number of possible experiments in brackets.

TABLE 3-1

| Target | ← Unpolarized → | | ← Polarized → | | |
Beam	Un- polarized	Polarized	Un- polarized	Polarized	Total
Cross section	$\sigma(1)$	$e(3)$	(3)	(9)	(16)
Polarization	$P(3)$	D, R, A, A' R' (9)	(9)	(27)	(48)
Polarization (recoil)	(3)	$D_t(9)$	(9)	(27)	(48)
Correlation	$C_{nn}(9)$ C_{qp}	(27)	(27)	(81)	(144)
Total	(16)	(48)	(48)	(144)	(256)

The same considerations on the number of experiments may be expressed more formally, but in a form less useful experimentally, by noting that the spin state of the two particles is determined by the expectation values of the 16 independent matrices. $\sigma_\mu^{(1)}\sigma_\nu^{(2)}$, where σ_1, σ_2, σ_3, σ_0 are the Pauli spin matrices and the unit matrix, and the superscripts represent the 256 scalar coefficients

$$Z_{\mu\nu\lambda\rho}(\mathbf{k}, \mathbf{k}') = \tfrac{1}{4}Tr\sigma_\mu^{(1)}\sigma_\nu^{(2)}M(\mathbf{k}, \mathbf{k}')\sigma_\lambda^{(1)}\sigma_\rho^{(2)}M^*(\mathbf{k}, \mathbf{k}') \quad (3\text{-}3)$$

and M is a general scattering matrix (MacGregor, 1960). Note that we now use σ as a spin operator as well as its previous use as a cross section. The difference should be obvious from the context.

The notation of the experiments is that of Wolfenstein (1956). Thus $\sigma(\theta)$ is the differential cross section. $P(\theta)$ is the polarization produced by the unpolarized beam in the scattering. $e(\theta)$, the asymmetry in scattering of a polarized proton beam is defined by

$$e(\theta) = \frac{C(\theta) - C(-\theta)}{C(\theta) + C(-\theta)} \quad (3\text{-}4)$$

where $C(\theta)$ and $C(-\theta)$ are the scattered counts at angles θ and $-\theta$.

Of course the total number of experiments to be performed at one angle and energy (256) is too many for a practical solution. We must therefore find some simplifying feature or features. Firstly, parity conservation, if true, limits the possibilities. The scattering matrix can only include scalar quantities and must exclude pseudoscalar quantities. The spin vector is a pseudovector, so that a scalar can only be formed by a scalar product with another pseudovector or axial vector. Bilinear functions of the same spin vector are linear functions.

The other vectors in the problem are the incident and final momenta $\mathbf{k}$, $\mathbf{k}'$. From these we may form three convenient orthogonal vectors $\mathbf{q} = \mathbf{k}' - \mathbf{k}$ the momentum transfer, a polar vector, $\mathbf{p} = \mathbf{k}' + \mathbf{k}$ a polar vector, and $\mathbf{n} = \mathbf{k} \times \mathbf{k}'$, the normal to the scattering plane, an axial vector or pseudovector. We denote by σ_{1n} the scalar product $\boldsymbol{\sigma}_1 \cdot \mathbf{n}$ and so forth for other suffices.

The following independent products then form scalar functions:

$$1, \sigma_{1n}\sigma_{2n}, \sigma_{1n} + \sigma_{2n}, \sigma_{1n} - \sigma_{2n}, \sigma_{1p}\sigma_{2p}, \sigma_{1q}\sigma_{2q},$$

$$\sigma_{1q}\sigma_{2p}, \sigma_{1p}\sigma_{2q}, (\boldsymbol{\sigma}_1 \times \boldsymbol{\sigma}_2)\cdot\mathbf{n} \quad (3\text{-}5)$$

Other products, $\boldsymbol{\sigma}_1\cdot\boldsymbol{\sigma}_2$ for example, may be formed by linear combinations of these. $\sigma_{1p}, \sigma_{2p}, \sigma_{1q}, \sigma_{2q}$ are pseudoscalars and make the scattering matrix change sign under the parity operation.

Secondly, we may consider time reversal invariance. The time reversal transformation may be summarized by

$$\boldsymbol{\sigma} \rightarrow -\boldsymbol{\sigma} \qquad \mathbf{k} \rightarrow -\mathbf{k}' \qquad \mathbf{k}' \rightarrow -\mathbf{k}\cdot$$

whence

$$\mathbf{q} \rightarrow \mathbf{q} \qquad \mathbf{n} \rightarrow -\mathbf{n} \qquad \mathbf{p} \rightarrow -\mathbf{p}\cdot$$

Under the transformation the scattering matrix must not change sign. This rules out the products

$$(\boldsymbol{\sigma}_1 \times \boldsymbol{\sigma}_2)\cdot\mathbf{n}, \qquad \sigma_{1p}\sigma_{2q}, \qquad \sigma_{1q}\sigma_{2p}$$

Thus the most general form of the scattering matrix of two spin $\frac{1}{2}$ particles is given by

$$M(q) \equiv A(q) + B(q)\sigma_{1n}\sigma_{2n} + C(q)(\sigma_{1n} + \sigma_{2n})$$

$$+ D(q)(\sigma_{1n} - \sigma_{2n}) + E(q)\sigma_{1q}\sigma_{2q} + F(q)\sigma_{1p}\sigma_{2p} \quad (3\text{-}6)$$

If the forces between two nucleons are charge symmetric, as is certainly the case for pp scattering, the quantity D vanishes. This follows because the interchange of the two particles must leave M unaltered. This leaves ten quantities to be determined; the real and imaginary parts of A, B, C, E, and F. As an example of this simplification, it can be noted that a beam can be polarized in scattering only along the direction $\mathbf{n}$, and not along the other directions $\mathbf{p}$ and $\mathbf{q}$. This reduces the number of possible, and necessary, experiments in the appropriate squares from three to one. The number of experiments studying the polarization after scattering of a polarized beam is reduced from 27 to 5 of which only three are independent.

A further reduction is made by an extension of the optical theorem of equations (3-1) and (3-2) which may be proved by requiring that the scattering matrix be unitary (Pushikov, 1956). These are

$$(4\pi/k)\,\mathrm{Im}\,A(\mathbf{k}, \mathbf{k}') = \int M^*(\mathbf{k}, \mathbf{k}'')M(\mathbf{k}'', \mathbf{k}')d\mathbf{k}''$$

$$(4\pi/k)\,\mathrm{Im}\,B(\mathbf{k}, \mathbf{k}') = \int M^*(\mathbf{k}, \mathbf{k}'')\sigma_{1n}\sigma_{2n}M(\mathbf{k}'', \mathbf{k}')d\mathbf{k}''$$

$$(2\pi/k)\,\mathrm{Re}\,C(\mathbf{k}, \mathbf{k}') = \int M^*(\mathbf{k}, \mathbf{k}'')(\sigma_{1n} + \sigma_{2n})M(\mathbf{k}'', \mathbf{k}')d\mathbf{k}''$$

$$(4\pi/k)\,\mathrm{Im}\,E(\mathbf{k}, \mathbf{k}') = \int M^*(\mathbf{k}, \mathbf{k}'')\sigma_{1p}\sigma_{2p}M(\mathbf{k}'', \mathbf{k}')d\mathbf{k}''$$

$$(4\pi/k)\,\mathrm{Im}\,F(\mathbf{k}, \mathbf{k}') = \int M^*(\mathbf{k}, \mathbf{k}'')\sigma_{1q}\sigma_{2q}M(\mathbf{k}'', \mathbf{k}')d\mathbf{k}'' \qquad (3\text{-}7)$$

Thus only five experiments need be made provided they are made at all angles at the one energy to determine the 10 constants. This statement, of course, is a general one. With a particular set of five experiments there may still be, for example, an ambiguity of sign of one phase shift. It also seems inconsistent with the knowledge from Chapter 2 that at low energies only one experiment, a measurement of the cross section, at any angle, determines all that can be found out about pp scattering, the $^1S_0$ state phase shift. For np scattering two numbers are wanted, the $^1S_0$ and the ^3S state phase shifts. A measurement of the cross section at any angle only determines an average of these and the polarization is identically zero. A measurement of the correlation coefficient C_{nn} can tell directly the relative amounts of singlet and triplet scattering. (It should be noted that the relative amounts of singlet and triplet scattering are, in fact, as discussed earlier, determined by an experiment not falling in this framework; the coherent molecular scattering.) The five experiments at all angles seem unnecessary. Yet this is only true because *a priori* knowledge is used about the range of nuclear forces and hence the energy at which the interaction in the different angular momentum states becomes important.

Time reversal invariance leads to a simplification of Table 3-1. It may be seen by an application of the density matrix (Wolfenstein, 1956) that the polarization $P(\theta)$ produced in the scattering of an unpolarized beam at an angle θ, is the same as the asymmetry $e(\theta)$ of the scattering of a completely polarized beam. In general, the experiments on opposite sides of the leading diagonal in Table 3-1 are equivalent.

If a double scattering experiment is performed, the polarization after the first scattering is $P(\theta)$. If a second identical scattering follows, the overall asymmetry becomes

$$P(\theta)e(\theta) = [P(\theta)]^2 \tag{3-8a}$$

The structure of this formula may be understood most clearly by considering each scattering as a selection process. An unpolarized beam is a mixture of two beams of opposite polarization. The scattering cross sections for particles of one polarization are $\sigma(\theta)[1 + e(\theta)]$ for angle θ and $\sigma(\theta)[1 - e(\theta)]$ for angle $-\theta$, where the $\pm$ signs refer to the two directions of polarization of the beam. After scattering, an equal mixture gives therefore a polarization

$$\frac{1 + e(\theta) - [1 - e(\theta)]}{2} = e(\theta)$$

in agreement with the general rule from time reversal.

Once we wish to take advantage of the simplicity given by the assumption of parity and time reversal invariance it is convenient to use a different formalism more suited to discussion of experiments. This was, in fact, the original formalism of Wolfenstein. In a scattering of an unpolarized particle, the direction of the resultant polarization can only be perpendicular to the scattering plane because only the factor $\sigma_{1n} = \boldsymbol{\sigma}_1 \cdot \mathbf{n}$ can give a scalar term in the interaction.

We may consider the polarization after the second scattering of a particle which has components of an incident polarization P_{1n}, P_{1t} and P_{1e} along the normal to the scattering plane, transverse to both this normal and the beam and along the beam. This separation is obviously simple from an experimental point of view, though it will raise algebraic complications when we wish to compare it with the scattering matrix equation (3-6). We can look, for polarizations along the normal to the scattering plane, and transverse (t') and longitudinal (l') to the scattered particle. The analyser, like the polarizer, only analyses polarizations in one direction perpendicular to its plane ($\mathbf{n}_3$) with a power $P(\theta_3)$. An analysis normal to $\mathbf{n}_2$ then gives, in general, an asymmetry

$$e_n = [P_{1n}D(\theta_2) + P_{1t}M(\theta_2) + P_{1l}N(\theta_2) + P_2(\theta_2)]P_3(\theta_3) \quad \text{(3-8b)}$$

It is easy to see that the coefficients of P_{1t} and P_{1l} vanish for a parity conserving reaction either by direct calculation with the matrix (3-7) or by direct consideration of the parity operator on (3-8b). This leaves only two terms the second of which has already been measured by a double scattering experiment.

Measurement along the transverse direction (t') gives

$$e_{t'} = [P_{1n}0(\theta_2) + P_{1t}R(\theta_2) + P_{1l}A(\theta_2) + P_2'(\theta_2)]P_3(\theta_3) \quad \text{(3-9)}$$

measurement along the longitudinal direction gives

$$e_{l'} = [P_{1n}Q(\theta_2) + P_{1t}R'(\theta_2) + P_{1l}A'(\theta_2) + P''(\theta_2)]P_3(\theta_3) \quad \text{(3-10)}$$

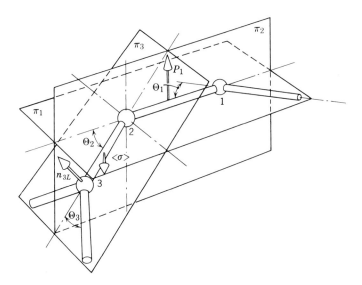

Figure 3-1. Schematic diagram of the scattering planes for measurement of the rotation parameter R (from Chamberlain).

we here define the 9 parameters, D, R, A, R', A', M, N, O, Q of the appropriate box of Table 3-1 and 3 parameters of a double scattering box. P', P'', M, N, O, Q must all vanish if parity is conserved. The letters D and R stand for depolarization and rotation, the appropriate effect on the spin being measured. Figure 3-1 shows the scattering planes used to measure the parameter R in (3-9).

We may define similarly the correlation parameter C_{nn} in which analyzers (power P_1 and P_2) measure perpendicular to the scattering plane, and the asymmetry

$$e_{nn} = P_1 P_2 C_{nn} \qquad (3\text{-}11)$$

is measured. Clearly in such an experiment, the asymmetry can be measured by rotating either of the polarization analysers through $180°$. Rotation of both should reach the same counting rate.

The C_{nnn} is a measure of the same correlation with an incident beam polarized along the normal to the scattering plane. C_{qp} and $C_{(n \times q)np}$ have obvious meanings.

The relation between the experimental parameters and the Wolfenstein matrix, equation (2-6), is given in Table 3-2. See also Stapp (1956), MacGregor (1960), Wolfenstein (1956). A tabulation of the quantities measurable with polarized targets in terms of elements of the scattering matrix is given by Schumacher (1961).

TABLE 3-2   MEASURED QUANTITIES IN TERMS OF THE
ELEMENTS OF THE SCATTERING MATRIX

$\sigma_0 = |A|^2 + |B|^2 + 2|C|^2 + |E|^2 + |F|^2$

$\sigma_0 P = 2 \operatorname{Re} C^*(A + B)$

$\sigma_0(1 - D) = 2E^2 + 2F^2 = G^2 + H^2$

$\qquad (G = E + F)$

$\qquad (H = E - F)$

$\sigma_0 R = [A^2 - B^2 + \operatorname{Re} HG^*]\cos\theta/2 - 2\operatorname{Im} C(A^* - B^*)\sin\theta/2$

$\sigma_0 A = -[A^2 - B^2 + \operatorname{Re} HG^*]\sin\theta/2 - 2\operatorname{Im} C(A^* - B^*)\cos\theta/2$

$\sigma_0 R' = (A^2 - B^2 - \operatorname{Re} GH^*)\sin\theta/2 + 2\operatorname{Im} C(A^* - B^*)\cos\theta/2$

$\sigma_0 A' = (A^2 - B^2 - \operatorname{Re} GH^*)\cos\theta/2 - 2\operatorname{Im} C(A^* - B^*)\sin\theta/2$

$\sigma_0 C_{qp} = +2 \operatorname{Im} CH^*$

$\sigma_0(1 - C_{nn}) = |A - B|^2 + G^2$

$\sigma_0 C_{nnn} = \operatorname{Re} C(A^* + B^*)$

$\sigma_0 C_{nqp} = \operatorname{Im}[(A - B)G^* - (A + B)H^*]$

$\sigma_0 C_{(n \times q)np} = \cos(\theta/2)\operatorname{Im}[(A + B)G^* - (A - B)H^*] + 2\sin(\theta/2)\operatorname{Re} CG^*$

3.2   Impulse Approximation for Proton-Neutron Scattering

Although it is, in principle, possible to perform an adequate number of experiments by scattering free protons off free protons and free neutrons off free protons, many of the experiments necessary to give a complete understanding are inconvenient. It therefore becomes necessary to understand a little of the theory of the scattering from the deuteron so that the neutron in the deuteron may be used as a target in proton-neutron scattering experiments.

The idea behind the approximation is the observation, that the "radius" of the deuteron $1/\gamma = 4 \times 10^{-13}$ cms from (2-4) is larger than the range of nuclear forces 1.7×10^{-13} cms. Thus the proton and neutron spend a large part of their time outside each other's influence. If then an incoming particle of wavelength $\lambda \ll 4 \times 10^{-13}$ cms is incident, the deuteron can behave like two independent particles. The effect of the binding is to impart a motion to the struck nucleon so that it is not completely stationary before collision. It is necessary not only that the wavelength of the incident nucleon be less than the radius of the deuteron, but also that the reciprocal of the momentum transfer $1/q$ be less than the radius of the deuteron. This gives

$$q = \frac{2 \sin \frac{1}{2}\theta}{\lambda} \gg \gamma \qquad (3\text{-}12)$$

This is the usual condition for incoherent scattering.

If the condition (3-12) is met, we may reasonably expect the scattering of protons by deuterons to be given to a good approximation, by the sum of scattering by a neutron and by a proton. If further, one of the struck particles is measured in coincidence, the scattering can be identified as a pn or a pp scattering. The distribution in momentum of the struck nucleon is simply the square of the wavefunction of the deuteron in momentum space. The probability of finding a nucleon with a momentum p is therefore the Fourier transform of the asymptotic deuteron wavefunction $e^{-\gamma r}$;

i.e., it is

$$\phi^2(p) = 4\pi N_g{}^2 \left(\frac{1}{\gamma^2 + p^2/\hbar^2}\right)^2$$

$$= \frac{8\pi\gamma}{1 - \gamma\rho(-\epsilon, -\epsilon)} \left(\frac{1}{\gamma^2 + p^2/\hbar^2}\right) \qquad (3\text{-}13)$$

When the struck nucleon has close to zero momentum the kinematics is close to the free particle kinematics. It can, never, however, be exactly so, because of the binding of the deuteron.

Chew and Low (1959) were the first to observe that at the (unphysical) point where the struck particle momentum is given by $p^2 = -\gamma^2/\hbar^2$, energy and momentum conservation give the same conditions as the free particle scattering and the scattering amplitude has a pole (is infinite), due to the pole in (3-13). At this pole the simple approximation is exact if we neglect final state interactions. They therefore suggest that the cross section be measured at various points corresponding to different struck momenta p, and that an extrapolation be performed to $p^2 = -\hbar^2\gamma^2$.

In practice this extrapolation is not convenient, the extrapolation function is not specified and the loss of statistical accuracy involved is intolerable. The procedure adopted, therefore, has been to verify the validity of the simple theory in some cases. Thus it is possible to identify pp scattering by a coincidence measurement. Extensive studies [Kuckes (1961), Tinlot (1961)] show that it is reasonable to use the uncorrected impulse approximation for polarization measurements to a few percent, but that it is incorrect for differential cross section measurements by about 10% if kinematics close to the free particle kinematics are employed, and by more if the kinematics are not close to free particle kinematics.

Attempts are also being made to calculate the corrections to the simple approximation (Chew, 1951, Everett, 1962). The difficulty lies in that the second order correction is small for the collisions in which the nucleons in the deuteron lie far apart initially, but of the order of the effect itself for those in which they are close together. Thus there is difficulty in carrying out an expansion.

More reliable attempts are being made by Cromer (1963). The scattering amplitude in the simple approximation is the sum of two terms. One is the desired pn scattering with the pole just discussed; the other is pp scattering with a pole near zero corresponding to an ability to distinguish the spectator particle. The final state interactions are calculated exactly for the $^3S \rightarrow {}^1S$ and $^3S \rightarrow {}^3S$ transitions in each term, and neglected for the higher angular momentum states. The extrapolation procedure of Chew and Low no longer works, so this method of calculation is essential.

The impulse approximation in another limit—when

$$q \ll \gamma \qquad (3\text{-}14)$$

yet

$$1/\lambda \gg \gamma \qquad (3\text{-}15)$$

gives elastic scattering from the deuteron. This is discussed further in Chapter 9.

For the pn triple scattering experiment it is necessary, to ensure adequate intensity, to integrate over a range around the pole and thus to allow more terms to enter the scattering. The double scattering experiments have a cleaner separation.

3.3   Use of Charge Independence

For the np scattering we may perform the set of five experiments at all angles 0°–180° cm to determine the scattering matrix. However, it is hard to obtain enough data. It is more usual therefore to use the assumption of charge independence. We observed in Chapter 2 that the interactions of protons with protons and neutrons with protons are almost the same in similar states. The assumption that this is exactly true is called charge independence and is discussed further in Chapter 8. If we assume it is exactly true we have already some information about np scattering from pp scattering. It is usual to describe this in the isotopic spin system whereby the neutron and proton are two states $T_z = \pm\frac{1}{2}$ of a $T = \frac{1}{2}$ particle. Two protons form a triplet $T = 1$ state and a neutron and proton can exist either in $T = 0$ or $T = 1$ state. The assumption of charge independence corresponds to conservation of total isotopic spin T in a reaction in the same way as conservation of J corresponds to conservation of angular momentum.

Then we may, following Feldman (1953) and Jacobsohn (1953), consider the following three reactions:

$$p_1 + p_2 \rightarrow p_3 + p_4$$
$$n_1 + p_2 \rightarrow n_3 + p_4$$
$$n_1 + p_2 \rightarrow p_3 + n_4 \qquad (3\text{-}16)$$

where n and p denote neutron and proton, respectively. We denote charge triplet ($T = 1$) amplitudes by f and singlet ($T = 0$) by g. With appropriate normalization, and neglecting Coulomb effects, the cross sections for the three processes become

$$\sigma_{pp}(\theta) = |f|^2$$
$$\sigma_{np}(\theta) = \tfrac{1}{4}|f + g|^2$$
$$\sigma_{pn}(\theta) = \tfrac{1}{4}|f - g|^2 \qquad (3\text{-}17)$$

f and g are functions of momentum and spin variables. We can see at once for example

$$2[\sigma_{np}(\theta) + \sigma_{pn}(\theta)] - \sigma_{pp} = |g|^2 \qquad (3\text{-}18)$$

and noting that $\sigma_{np}(\theta) = \sigma_{np}(\pi - \theta)$ in the cm system, we derive a "cross section" for $T = 0$ states

$$2[\sigma_{np}(\theta) + \sigma_{np}(\pi - \theta)] - \sigma_{pp} = |g|^2 = \sigma_{(T=0)} \qquad (3\text{-}19)$$

we may derive similar relations for the polarization P and the triple scattering parameters D, R, A.

$$2[P\sigma_{np}(\theta) + P\sigma_{np}(\pi - \theta)] - P\sigma_{pp} = P\sigma_{(T=0)}$$
$$2[D\sigma_{np}(\theta) + D_t\sigma_{np}(\pi - \theta)] - D\sigma_{pp} = D\sigma_{(T=0)} \qquad (3\text{-}20)$$

We see here some inequalities that must be satisfied for charge independence to hold given by $|g|^2 > 0$. As can easily be seen from the data in subsequent chapters, they hold quite well. These relations are of limited utility for they *still* require five experiments over the angular range! The problem is that the information in the interference terms has been neglected. Thus we have

$$\sigma_{np}(\theta) - \sigma_{np}(\pi - \theta) = (\mathrm{Re}\, f^*\, g)/2 \qquad (3\text{-}21)$$

Thus it is reasonable to hope that five experiments over the region $0 - \pi/2$ or $2\frac{1}{2}$ over the region $0 - \pi$ should be enough to give a solution for the np interaction once the np system is known. This much information is now available. Relations such as (3-20) may aid direct understanding of the processes, however, and avoid the necessity for the somewhat arbitrary phase shift analysis.

Chapter 4

High-Energy Experiments— Apparatus

Two types of accelerator have been used to produce protons; cyclotrons at energies up to 700 mev and linear accelerators up to 70 mev. The linear accelerator has a very clear advantage, in that the beam is extracted without effort and the energy spread and size of the beam are small—about $\frac{1}{2}\%$ and a few mm.

Moreover the energy may be more easily varied. However, the ease of construction and the reliability is less and the duty cycle is fixed at about $\frac{1}{100}$. Recently various methods have led to cyclotron beams with a duty cycle of $\frac{1}{2}$. Table 4-1 lists the accelerators used in this work. The names in capitals are the common appellations used in the text.

4.1 Cyclotrons: Beam Extraction

With cyclotrons the problem arises of extracting the beam. The energy associated with free radial oscillations of the cyclotron beam is quite large, radial oscillation amplitudes being up to 8 cm. The vertical aperture is usually limited, because the cost of the magnet is proportional to the aperture, so that vertical amplitudes are limited to 2 cm. Any coupling between these two amplitudes leads to loss of the beam in a vertical direction. Such a coupling, first found on the Berkeley 184 in. cyclotron (Henrich, 1949), has been observed in every frequency modulated cyclotron since at a radius

TABLE 4-1   ACCELERATORS USED IN NUCLEON-NUCLEON
SCATTERING AT HIGH ENERGIES. THE NAME IN CAPITALS,
IN THE LOCATION, IS THE COMMON APPELLATION USED IN
THE TEXT

Max. Energy	Type	Location
10 mev	Linac (Bevatron injector)	Lawrence Radiation Laboratory BERKELEY, California
18 mev	Cyclotron	PRINCETON University Princeton, New Jersey
32 mev	Linac	Lawrence Radiation Laboratory BERKELEY, California
50 mev	Linac	Rutherford Laboratory National Inst. for Nuclear Research HARWELL, Berks, England
70 mev	Linac	University of Minnesota Minneapolis, MINNESOTA
160 mev	Cyclotron	Laboratoire de la Physique Nucleaire, Universite de Paris ORSAY, France
165 mev	Cyclotron	HARVARD University Cambridge 38, Massachusetts
165 mev	Cyclotron	Atomic Energy Research Establishment HARWELL, Berks, England
180 mev	Cyclotron	University of Upsala UPSALA, Sweden
240 mev	Cyclotron	University of Rochester ROCHESTER, New York
380 mev	Cyclotron	University of Liverpool LIVERPOOL, England
400 mev	Cyclotron	CARNEGIE Inst. of Technology Pittsburgh, Pennsylvania
400 mev	Cyclotron	University of Chicago CHICAGO, Illinois
400 mev	Cyclotron	COLUMBIA University Irvington-on-Hudson, New York
660 mev	Cyclotron	Joint Institute for Nuclear Research DUBNA, Russia, U.S.S.R.
700 mev	Cyclotron	Lawrence Radiation Laboratory BERKELEY, California

about 1 cm less than the maximum stable radius. The system of beam extraction must extract the beam before this resonant radius, and be so designed that the vertical motion remains stable. Such a system was suggested by Tuck and worked out analytically by LeCouteur.

Several applications of the method have now been made (Tuck, 1951, LeCouteur, 1955, Crewe, 1955, Calame, 1957). With this method about 8% of the internal beam has been extracted. It has been shown by Calame et al., that the trajectories of the external beam are appreciably different for particles of different initial amplitudes of radial oscillation. So also are the equilibrium radii of the particles at the moment of extraction and hence their energy and the time of extraction. For a typical cyclotron, the energy spread of the beam is about 5 mev (independent of the cyclotron radius and mean energy) corresponding to an 8 cm spread in radial oscillation amplitudes. The time spread will depend upon the rate of change of frequency with time but would be of the order of 100 μsec. By contrast, the beam striking an internal target, without any extraction procedure, has an energy spread of 15 mev, and a time spread of 300 μsec.

Some cyclotrons have reported smaller energy spreads (1 mev) and therefore smaller time spreads (20 μsec) than those quoted above, but it is probable that this is due to a selection of the particle orbits after the main extraction procedure. Such a selection can always be introduced intentionally, with the appropriate reduction in overall beam intensity.

4.2 Cyclotrons: Duty Cycle

The radio frequency may be switched off just before the end of the acceleration cycle. Then a target may be mechanically moved into the beam from (say) a vertical direction. The time spread of the beam will now be the time for the target to intercept all particles no matter what their oscillation amplitudes, or approximately the amplitude of vertical oscillation divided by the velocity of the target. This can be adjusted to be $\frac{1}{4}$ of the time between beam pulses giving a duty cycle of $\frac{1}{4}$. The fine structure also tends to disappear, for without rf there can be no synchrotron stability. At the time of writing this method has been successfully tried at Liverpool, Columbia, CERN, and at Harwell.

If the rf is switched off quickly, the energy spread of the beam striking the target should be quite small, limited only by the spread of synchronous oscillations.

There is another method, or rather class of methods of improving the duty cycle. After the main radio frequency acceleration has been switched off as in the first method, the beam is accelerated the last few centimeters by an auxiliary dee. This method has several variants, according to the frequency and voltage to be placed on the auxiliary dee. The simplest idea, conceptually, is to have a similar frequency to the main dee, but let it change with time a factor of 10 slower. It is easy to see that the duty cycle will then improve by a factor of 10. It will not matter if at the end of the auxiliary FM cycle acceleration has started again with the main dee; the frequency will not be correct for acceleration, and the effect on the beam at the end of the acceleration will be incoherent.

Since the energy increase per turn is small, when the frequency change is small, the rf may be reduced by the same factor of 10; or else the angular width of the dee may be reduced. The auxiliary oscillator can also be run at a harmonic of the cyclotron frequency enabling the angular width to be further reduced and making the mechanical problems of finding space for such a dee simpler.

It is also possible to use other frequency variations than the simple extension of the ordinary cyclotron frequency-time curve. The extreme in this respect is to use stochastic acceleration, first discussed by Veksler (1958), and proposed for this application by Keller (1959). By so doing, no fine structure of the beam will remain.

The applications so far are at Orsay by Cabrespine (1960), and at Liverpool. It is more flexible than the first, for the first only works with an internal target and not an extracted beam.

4.3 Polarized Beams by Scattering

The accelerators described above do not in themselves polarize the beam. Yet it is clear from the discussion of Chapter 3 that polarized beams are essential.

The first method of polarization depends basically upon the process itself. It is clear from equation (3-5) that if there is an asymmetry in the scattering of a polarized beam (dependence of cross section upon polarization) then there is an equal polarization. This polarization will be limited by, parity conservation, to the normal to the scattering plane. In practice it is inconvenient to use a hydrogen target in the cyclotron, and to rely on the polarization in pp scattering. It has been found (see Chapter 10 infra) that light nuclei also polarize the beam, and in fact more strongly than does hydrogen at the energies we are concerned with. A target of carbon or beryllium is therefore almost always used. The polarization of the beam is found in an auxiliary experiment using equation (3-5) ($e^2 = P_1 P_2$). In practice several small corrections must be made to this formula. First of all, it is necessary to have an appreciable target thickness to obtain a finite counting rate, and then the two scatterings are not at the same energy. The polarization varies slowly and smoothly with energy so that a correction is easily deduced. After the polarization has been measured for one angle and element, the first scattering angle need no longer be changed.

We note from equation (3-5) that the sign cannot be so determined. Two methods exist for determining the sign. A proton beam may be slowed down to a few mev and scattered in helium (Marshall, 1955, Brinkworth, 1956) where the low energy scattering data already imply a separation of the $P^{3/2}$ and $P^{1/2}$ levels in the He^5 and Li^5 $T = \frac{1}{2}$ states, and therefore that there will be large polarizations in scattering at this energy region. The order of the levels is known and hence the sign of the polarization.

For neutron beams another method is available, both for measuring the sign and magnitude of the polarization. The nuclear scattering of neutrons from heavy nuclei is described principally by an imaginary scattering amplitude, given by the optical theorem (3-1), from the easily measured total cross section. There is in addition a scattering due to the interaction of the neutron's magnetic moment with the Coulomb field, which gives an imaginary spin dependent amplitude and is completely calculable. The polarization is near 100% for $\theta_{\text{lab}} = \frac{1}{4}°$ and $E_{\text{lab}} = 90$ mev. Such beam measurements have been made by Voss (1956) following the suggestion of Schwinger (1948). They are now standard practice for polarized neutron beam work. The two methods of sign measurement are not independent and may be compared by experiments on np scattering and pn scattering (Chapter 6). They agree.

In practice proton beams of 90% polarization may be obtained at 210 mev and smaller at lower energies; Figure 10-7 shows the maximum attainable polarization. This method is clearly not useful below 100 mev.

4.4   Neutron Beams

Neutron beams are always produced by charge exchange. As will be seen, pn scattering gives a large peak near 180° cm (0° neutron angle). This is also present in light nuclei. In principle it should be possible to use the reaction $p(d, 2p)n$ to produce the neutrons. Due to the low binding energy of the deuteron and the interaction of the protons in the singlet state, this gives a sharp energy distribution (Bowen, 1960, Esten, 1960). Unfortunately the targets are usually internal in a cyclotron and deuterium is an inconvenient choice. Even in a light element such as beryllium, the internal motion of the nucleons spreads out the energies somewhat more than in the deuteron. Also, multiple collisions add a low energy tail.

If the neutrons are not taken in the forward direction they may be polarized. Indeed, according to the simplest picture, they would be expected to have the same polarization as in free pn scattering independent of target element. This picture predicts (see infra) polarizations increasing with energy from 8% at 100 mev to 30% at 350 mev at 30° lab. At larger angles, the polarization would change sign according to this simple picture. In fact it does not, and is actually greater ($\sim$30%) at 50° lab than the free pn polarization. (Carpenter, 1959, Bowen, 1961, 1962). Thus we see that the ordinary method of producing a neutron beam can also give a polarized beam.

4.5 Polarized Ion Sources

Various proposals have been made for making a polarized ion source. They are all variants of each other, and we here describe the proposal of Abragam (1958). Figure 4-1 shows the energy levels of a hydrogen atom in a magnetic field. At high fields, the levels separate cleanly into those with electron spins along or against the field (states a and b vs. states c and d). A Stern-Gerlach experiment

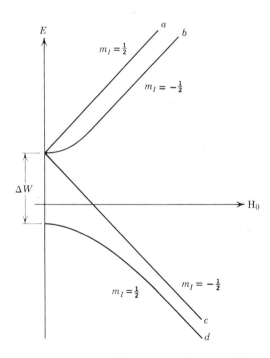

Figure 4-1. Energy levels of a hydrogen atom in an applied magnetic field (from Feld).

separates the states, or one pair can be focused and the other defo-
cused in a hexapole magnetic field. Suppose states a and b are thus
selected. Abragam suggested transferring all the atoms in state b
to state d by applying a radiofrequency field using the adiabatic
fast passage method. Then states with $M_I = \frac{1}{2}$ are selected, or the
protons are polarized 100%.

Alternatively, after selection of states a and b from c and d in a
strong field, a weak field separation may be used. Now state a may
be focused in a region where state b has no magnetic moment and
is not focused. Again, nearly 100% polarization may be achieved.
After polarization, the spin may be bent into any convenient direction by the use of quite small magnetic fields at the ionizer.

In practice the theoretical 100% polarization can be diluted by
inadequate defocusing of the unwanted states and by admixture
of unpolarized atoms in the ionizer. The polarization obtained can
therefore be a variable and depend on accelerator operation.

So far, polarized ion sources have been successfully used only on
proton linear accelerators at Harwell (Stafford, 1962), where 32%
polarization has been achieved, with an intensity of 7.5×10^7 protons per second, and at Minnesota with slightly less intensity.

If these polarized ions are used to inject into a cyclotron, it is
necessary to ensure that they do not depolarize in the acceleration
process. The question has been studied by Lobkowitz (1962) who
shows that the magnetic field inhomogeneities must be kept below
10^{-4}. This requirement is greater than any other for an ordinary
cyclotron. It is just met by the Harvard cyclotron, and just fails
for the Rochester cyclotron.

4.6   Targets—CH_2, CD_2

At high energies, the range of the protons is quite large, and it is
possible to use thick targets as compared to low-energy experiments. However, beam intensities, particularly of polarized beams,
are quite low, and the possibility becomes a necessity. The gas
target universally used at low energies (see, for example, Fig. 2-8)
has therefore only been used up to 70 mev at Minnesota.

All the early experiments at high energies were performed by scattering from polyethylene $(CH_2)^n$ targets. The background of scattered particles from the carbon must be assessed by scattering from carbon. The hydrogen scattering may be increased relative to the carbon scattering by taking advantage of the two body kinematics. Thus in pp scattering two protons may be detected in 90° coincidence (for relativistic kinematics this angle is reduced by a few degrees), or the energy of one proton may be accurately measured. Both these methods fail at small angles where one particle has too low an energy to be detected or to influence the kinematics.

4.7 Liquid Hydrogen Targets

Because of the need to measure at small angles and to maintain intensity, liquid hydrogen targets are now almost universally used. Even liquid hydrogen targets present a major problem at small angles. The container walls must be kept thin to avoid background scattering, yet they must be thick enough to provide thermal insulation if no vacuum is used or strength against collapse if the target is used in a vacuum. As of the date of writing, the thinnest target walls have been obtained with targets *in vacuo*, so this type will be discussed exclusively. For small angle scattering nuclei scatter as A^2, yet their weight goes as A. So *ceteris paribus* a light element is best for the walls. By now, MYLAR (Registered trademark of DuPont Company, first used by Nicolai, 1955) is almost universally used. It may be glued to itself and to metals with epoxy resins. Although differential expansion undoubtedly occurs, the Mylar appears to remain sufficiently plastic at low temperatures to prevent strain. A drawing of a target, used at Harvard, is shown in Figure 4-2.

It is, of course, possible to design a scattering experiment so that scattering from the walls is not detected. This was done with the use of the gas targets at low energies, by using defining slits. At higher energies it is better to use a scintillation counter to define the counting region, because protons will penetrate slit edges, giving uncertain definition. There are problems with this type of ex-

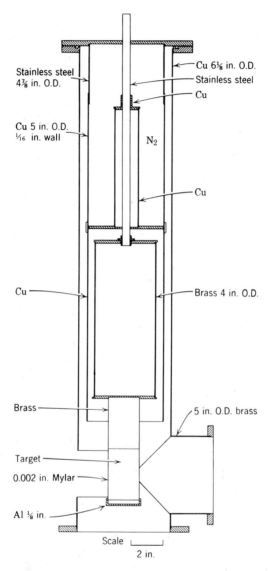

Figure 4-2. Liquid hydrogen target used for proton-proton cross section and
polarization measurements at HARVARD (Palmieri, 1958). Only small changes
are made for all other measurements.

periment, because the target varies with angle and it becomes more difficult to choose a geometry which optimizes counting rate.

In principle a solid hydrogen target could be used with no walls, or very thin walls merely to prevent evaporation. Such a target has never yet been tested.

4.8 Polarized Targets

It is obviously desirable to make a polarized target for experiments. The "brute force" procedure would be to apply a magnetic field to the target of liquid hydrogen and reduce the temperature so that $\mu H \gg kT$, where μ is the magnetic moment. This involves $T \simeq 10^{-5}°K$ for $H = 20,000$ gauss. An alternate procedure, now being attempted in many laboratories (Saclay, Oxford, Minnesota, Berkeley, Harvard) is to attempt dynamic nuclear polarization. The procedure has produced some polarization (Abragam, 1958, Abraham, 1959, Schmugge, 1962).

Figure 4-3 shows the levels in a magnetic field of a single electron spin loosely coupled to a nucleus of spin $\frac{1}{2}$. Full arrows denote allowed transitions. Saturation of the partially forbidden transition A at a frequency $\nu_e - \nu_n$ leads to the population distribution shown on the right of the figure. The resulting ratio of populations of nuclear substates is

$$x_1 = (2 + \Delta)/(2 - \Delta) = 1 + \Delta \qquad (4\text{-}1)$$

compared to the equilibrium ratio,

$$x_0 = 1 + \delta \qquad (4\text{-}2)$$

where Δ and δ are the electronic and nuclear Boltzmann factors $(h\nu_e/kT)$ and $(h\nu_n/kT)$. Saturation of B yields

$$x_2 = 1 - \Delta \qquad (4\text{-}3)$$

Thus A leads to a positive "enhancement" Δ/δ and B to a negative, $-\Delta/\delta$.

At temperatures of $1°K$ obtained by pumping liquid He^3, the electronic polarization Δ can be nearly 100% giving a large polar-

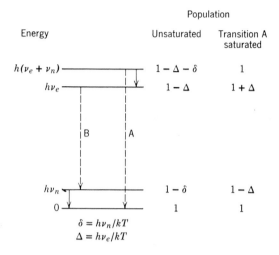

Figure 4-3. Levels in a magnetic field of a single electron spin loosely coupled to a nucleus of spin $\frac{1}{2}$.

ization. The polarization may be easily reversed by changing frequency or a small change in field, thus reducing experimental systematic errors arising from changing the beam alignment as counters are moved.

Factors leading to less than the polarization possible in principle include:

(1) Difficulty of obtaining the F centers to give the electron lines of Fig. 4-2.

(2) Broadening of the electron lines to a width larger than δ.

(3) Relaxation of the nuclear polarization too short.

So far a polarization of 5% of hydrogen in CH_2 and 50% of hydrogen in lanthanum magnesium nitrate has been reported. Solid deuterium is being studied. It seems that solid hydrogen will give too short a relaxation time to be useful. A working target of lanthanum magnesium nitrate has been used in a proton-proton scattering experiment. See Chapter 5 (Abragam, 1962).

4.9 Spin Precession by Magnets

The polarization by scattering is always transverse to the direction of motion. Yet to study some quantitites in (3-8), (3-9), (3-10) (A and A') it is necessary to produce longitudinal polarization. This may be done by using a magnet and allowing the spin to precess. The magnet is also useful for reversing the sign of polarization, and hence performing a polarization experiment without moving the apparatus or changing the background.

The precession of a particle in a magnetic field is, nonrelativistically, trivial and is the Larmor precession. We need a relativistic calculation which has been done most simply by Bargmann (1959). We are here concerned with his case $B(\mathbf{H} \cdot \mathbf{n} \times \mathbf{v} = H)$ with a magnetic field transverse to both the direction of motion and the spin direction; the spin is shown to precess into the direction of motion with a frequency $\Omega = \omega_L(g/2 - 1)$ where $\omega_L = (e/m\gamma)H$ is the Larmor precession frequency, g is the gyromagnetic ratio and $\gamma = (1 - v^2/c^2)^{-\frac{1}{2}}$. Then $\Omega = eH/m(g/2 - 1)$. Since $g/2$ is not equal to one for a proton or a neutron, there will be a precession. We wish to rotate the spin through $\pi/2$. If the velocity of the particle is v, then the length of the magnet required is given by

$$L = \frac{mv\pi}{eH(g - 2)} = \frac{mv\pi}{H(\mu - e)} \tag{4-4}$$

Nonrelativistically it can be easily estimated in terms of the deflection angle. The magnet deflects the spin $g\theta/2$ when the direction changes θ. We therefore need a deflection angle given by $(g/2 - 1)\theta = \pi/2$. Relativistically θ is reduced by γ. It is interesting to note that the length of magnet required is not prohibitive for any energy. For a proton ($g = 5.58$) and $H = 15$ kg, L becomes 3 ft for $v = \frac{1}{2}$ (150 mev) and is 6 ft at infinite energy.

It is also often convenient to use a magnet to allow the transverse polarization to precess from a vertical direction to a horizontal direction. This enables us to maintain the first scattering (inside the cyclotron) and the second scattering (with a variable angle and involving a liquid target) coplanar and yet to study the effects of a transverse polarization in the scattering plane (the Wolfenstein parameters R and R', equations (3-9) and (3-10)). We then need Bargmann's case A ($\mathbf{B} \times \mathbf{v} = 0$). This is achieved by an axial solenoid. The precession frequency is $\omega_L(g/2) = eHg/2m$. The magnet length required for a $\theta/2$ precession is now

$$L = (mv\gamma\pi/eHg) = (mv\gamma\pi/H) \qquad (4\text{-}5)$$

This differs from the first case by the factor γ in the numerator. We see that $\int Hdl = (mv\gamma\pi/\mu)$. A solenoid of 832,000 amp turns gives the correct value for 147 mev protons regardless of geometry. For neutrons a smaller coil may be used because of the larger value of μ. The first use of the solenoid was made, following a suggestion of the author, by Stafford (1957). Bargmann's treatment can be made to apply to neutrons, for which g is infinite, by deriving equations (4-4) and (4-5) as before and letting e tend to zero and g to infinity.

4.10   Energy Measurement

a. Protons

The best method of measuring the energy of a charged particle is by measuring the bending in a magnetic field. Thus a measure of the magnetic field of a cyclotron, combined with a knowledge of the equilibrium radius at ejection, can determine the energy. In practice, however, this is not accurate enough, and a special measurement has to be made on an external beam. This has been done in a few cases. In most reported measurements of nucleon-nucleon scattering, however, the measurements are in terms of a secondary standard, the range of the particles in matter. The range cannot as yet be calculated exactly but involve an arbitrary constant, the average excitation potential of the substance. This in turn can be given by one measurement with a beam whose energy is determined; and we then have a versatile, though complicated, formula.

Measurements have been made at about 20 mev of the range of

protons in several materials to about 0.1% precision (Bichsel, 1957). This has been used to derive range energy relations by Sternheimer (1959, 1960). A correction to these tables is now in press. More extensive tables, but less accurate and differing in range for the same energy by 1% and energy for the same range by $\frac{1}{2}$%, have been computed (Aaron, 1951, Rich, 1954). The corrected Sternheimer values are very close to the Aaron and Rich values.

An error in energy of $\frac{1}{2}$% can lead to an effective error in cross section of $\frac{1}{2}$% which at the present moment is small, except for measurements in the Coulomb interference region. Thus a measurement of range is usually quite adequate as a measure of energy.

Proton energies are now being measured by time of flight to a precision of 0.1% at the Harwell 50 mev linac.

b. Neutrons

The measurement of neutron energies is different. Two methods are used. When the neutrons are measured by observation of the proton recoil from np scattering, then the range of the proton recoil may be measured and combined with kinematics to give the neutron energy. This method of measuring the neutron energies can be successfully applied only for measurements taken between 40° and 180° cm or for attenuation (total cross section) measurements. This method is also combined with a selection of the energy by means of an absorber. Such a method is not, however, so useful at smaller angles.

The measurement of neutron energies by time of flight has been developed at Harwell (Scanlon, 1957, Bowen, 1962) and used in an extensive series of measurements. The cyclotron beam is deflected by a pulse vertically onto a target. The rise of the electrostatic pulse is timed with the radiofrequency to be when no particles are inside the electrodes, and the rise time of the pulse is small compared with a revolution. Under these circumstances the protons arrive at the target in a time interval $\simeq 5 \times 10^{-9}$ sec given by the rf synchronous stability. A pulse from the radiofrequency starts a time analyser. The time of flight over 30 m is measured. The apparatus is self-monitoring, for an instantaneous pulse is obtained from γ rays reaching the counter. A precision of ∼2% is achieved with a resolution in neutron energy of ∼5% at 150 mev. This method, like bending of a charged particle in a magnetic field, is absolute but has not yet been used to high precision. Time of flight was also used for the low-energy neutron work of Melkonian and of Squires (Table 2-2).

Chapter 5

Proton Measurements

5.1 Total Cross Sections

The measurement of total cross sections is made by an attenuation measurement. The apparatus of such an experiment is shown in Figure 5-1. The proton is detected by scintillation counters 1, 2

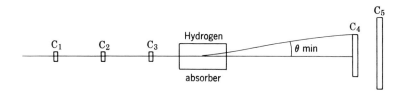

Figure 5-1. Experimental arrangement of measurement of *p-p* total cross section (schematic).

and 3 in coincidence and passes into the liquid hydrogen target. Afterwards, the unscattered protons reach the counters 4 and 5. Those scattering through an angle greater than θ (usually $\sim 5°$ to $20°$) are not detected. The experiment consists of comparing the coincidence rates 1 2 3 (C_1) and 1 2 3 4 5 (C_2). In the absence of liquid hydrogen they should be the same. In the presence of the hydrogen the difference becomes

$$(C_1 - C_2)/C_1 = \sigma \rho t L \qquad (5\text{-}1)$$

73

where σ is the cross section, ρ the density, t the target length and L is Avogadro's number.

There is a complicating feature; there is usually a difference $C_1 - C_2$ in the absence of liquid hydrogen due to absorption and scattering of protons in the scintillators, and to inefficiency of the coincidence circuits. The *difference* on addition of liquid hydrogen is the important quantity.

TABLE 5-1   TOTAL *p-p* SCATTERING CROSS SECTIONS

Author	Mean Energy (mev)	θ_{min} [b] cm	Cross Section Millibarns $= \int_{\theta_{min}}^{\pi/2} \frac{d\sigma}{d\pi} 2\pi \sin\theta \, d\theta$
Lindenbaum (1961) Brookhaven	5–20 [a]	0°	40–45
Ashmore (1960) CERN	10–28 [a]	0°	40–45
Diddens (1962) CERN	3–8 [a]	0°	40–45
von Dardel (1960) CERN	5–10 [a]	0°	41 ± 1
Longo (1959) Berkeley	1.400 [a]	0°	46.9 ± 0.8
	2.050 [a]	0°	45.0 ± 2
	4.000 [a]	0°	42.4 ± 0.6
Prokoshkin (1961) Dubna	500–640	0°	smooth to 0.1%
Chen (1956) Brookhaven	535	0°	29.8 ± 1.2
	830	0°	47.8 ± 1.5
	1,275	0°	47.5 ± 1.4
Law (1959) Birmingham	2,600	0°	41.6 ± 3.0
	1,010	0°	46.1 ± 0.5
Dzelephov Dubna	400–600	0°	27 to 41
Chamberlain (1954) Berkeley	330	20°	22.24 ± 0.70
	225	20°	21.30 ± 0.70
Taylor (1956) Harwell	134	0°	23.7 ± 0.9
Goloskie (1963) Harvard	147.2	12°	23.7 ± 0.2
	69.8	12°	38.7 ± 0.5

[a] Momentum in Bev/c.
[b] When $\theta_{min} = 0°$ the author has extrapolated his results to 0°.

At high energies, the experiment is trivial. The length of scatterer t may be such as to attenuate half or more of the protons so that a precise result may be obtained independent of these small effects and limited statistics. At low energies, however, the energy of the proton changes by an appreciable fraction on passing through the hydrogen and the length must be limited. $C_1 - C_2$ may be 10% or less of C_1.

If C_1 and C_2 are not measured *simultaneously* one then needs 10^6 counts to obtain 1% statistics in σ. However, C_1 and C_2 are measured simultaneously and it is only necessary for $C_1 - C_2$ to be 10^4 counts or C_1 10^5 counts. Small corrections must be applied for energy dependence of the spurious, target empty, value for $C_1 - C_2$. The results of existing measurements are in Table 5-1.

The total cross section may also be obtained by integrating the differential cross section $\int_{\theta_{\min}}^{90°} \frac{d\sigma}{d\Omega} \, d\Omega$. The two methods must, of course, agree.

An interesting relative measurement has been made by Prokoshkin (1961) to an accuracy of 0.1% using ionization chamber techniques. The energy of the incident proton beam was varied and two ionization chambers before and after the liquid hydrogen absorber were compared. The ratio was a smooth curve as a function of energy. We might expect a small cusp at a threshold for particle production. This was not observed.

5.2 Differential Cross Sections

The measurement of a differential cross section involves a measurement of three quantities: (*i*) the incident beam intensity; (*ii*) the target thickness and density; (*iii*) the counts corrected for efficiency and solid angle of the particle detecting telescope. A typical set up is shown in Figure 5-2. The external cyclotron beam is passed through an ionization chamber, an absorber if required for reducing the beam energy, the target, and then a Faraday cup. The charge is measured absolutely. The scattered particles are detected by a scintillation counter telescope. The beam intensity measurements are based on the Faraday cup. In some cases, however, the Faraday cup is removed while the measurements are in progress, and monitoring depends only on the ionization chamber. At Harwell, there is no Faraday cup, and the ionization chamber was calibrated by exposing photographic plates and counting the tracks.

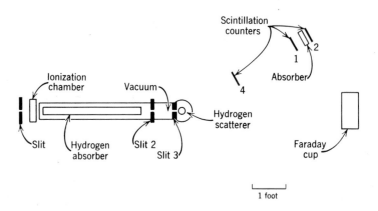

Figure 5-2. Experimental arrangement used by Palmieri (1958) for *p-p* cross section measurements.

In most of the differential cross section measurements the scintillation counter telescope can detect protons from all the target—including the walls. However, at Harwell, two scintillation counters were used to define a target and scattering from the target walls was not detected. At the energies below 60 mev, the target volume was defined by slits. In Figure 5-3 some typical angular distributions are shown, and in Figure 5-4 the differential cross section at 90° as a function of energy. In Figure 5-5 are shown typical angular distributions at a higher energy. Table 5-2 lists all available measurements.

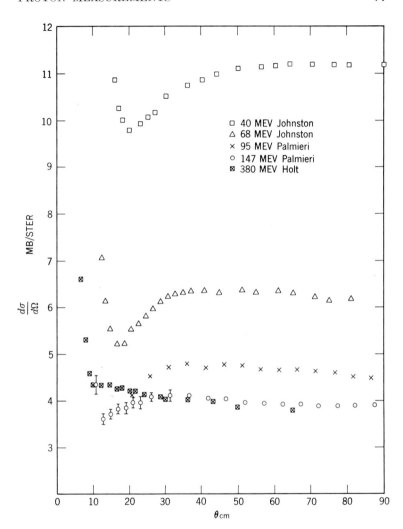

Figure 5-3. Angular distribution for *p-p* scattering from 40 to 380 mev.

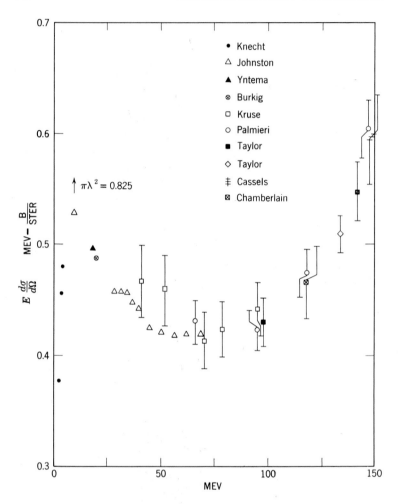

Figure 5-4. A plot of $E(d\sigma/d\Omega)_{90°}$ versus E for p-p scattering.

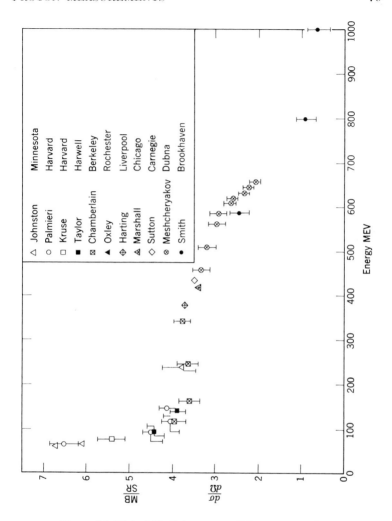

Figure 5-5. Plot of $(d\sigma/d\Omega)_{90°}$ versus E for p-p scattering.

TABLE 5-2   DIFFERENTIAL CROSS SECTION MEASUREMENTS [a]

Author	Energy mev	Angles cm	Absolute Precision %	Relative Precision %	Comments
Cork (1956) Berkeley	9.7	27°–90°	1	1	NaI counter, H_2 gas
Johnston (1958)	10	5°–90°	1	0.5	$d\Omega$ defined by
(1959) Minnesota	40	5°–90°	2	1	slits
Young (1960) Minnesota	68	5°–90°	2	1	Faraday cup monitoring
Jeong (1960) Minnesota	10–68	90°	2		
Yntema (1954) Princeton	18	30°–90°	1	0.5	
Kruse (1956) Harvard	95	20°–90°	—	3	Liq. H_2
	95	30°–90°	5	3	CH_2 coincidence
	40–95	90°	5		CH_2 coincidence
Palmieri (1958) Harvard	40–147	45°	5 [b]		Liq H_2,
	66	25°–90°	5 [b]	2	telescope,
	95	20°–90°	5 [b]	1	absorber
	118	20°–90°	5 [b]	1	
	147	20°–90°	5 [b]	1	
	147	6°–30°	—	1	
Taylor (1959) Harwell	95	6°–90°	5	3	Several runs
	142	6°–90°	5	3	normalized absorber used
Caversazio (1961) Orsay	155	6°–90°	4	1	No absorber used
Tinlot (1962) Rochester	213	20°–90°	—	2	CH_2, internal C^{11} monitoring
Chamberlain (1951) Berkeley	300	6°–20°	—	3	
Fischer (1954) Berkeley	330	4°–30°	—	3	Plate detection
Chamberlain (1951) Berkeley	330	20°–90°	5	2	CH_2 and Liq. H_2 targets
Holt (1958) Harting (1958) Liverpool	380	5°–90°	1½	1	CH_2 & Liq. H_2
Sutton (1955) Carnegie	437	17°–90°	5	2	CH_2 & Liq. H_2 Calib. ion chamber
Mescheriakov (1957) Dubna	460 660	5°–90°	5	3	
Smith (1955) Brookhaven	900– 3,000	15°–90°	10	10	CH_2 coincidence
Dowell (1960) Birmingham	1,010 ±10	18°–90°	—	5	CH_2—C coincidence
Preston (1960) Brookhaven	3,000	½°–5°	10	10	Liq. H_2
Cork (1957) Berkeley	3,000– 6,000	8°–90°	10	15	CH_2 coincidence
Cocconi (1961) CERN	13,000– 26,000	1°	20	20	CH_2—C single
Diddens (1962) CERN	12,000– 26,000	2°–43°	15	5	CH_2—C single liquid H_2
Baker (1962) Brookhaven	11,200 16,000	68.5° 77.5°	10 10	10 10	CH_2—C coincidence

[a] New measurements have been made by Nisimura (1963) at 52 mev; Fujii (1962) at 1 to 3 Bev; and Lindenbaum (1963) above 10 Bev.

[b] An error has been found in the absolute normalization of the Palmieri data of about 9% at 147 mev. The error at other energies is unknown. Accordingly we recommend ignoring the absolute normalization.

Some small disagreements exist between measurements. Thus Palmieri *et al.*, find that $(d\sigma/d\Omega)30°$ cm $> (d\sigma/d\Omega)90°$ cm at all energies from 68 to 147 mev. This agrees with Johnston, Kruse and Caversazio, but disagrees with Taylor who at both 95 and 142 mev finds the opposite inequality. The disagreement is about 4%. This may be due to relative changes in the Taylor data taken at different times. The recommendation is to *exclude* the Taylor data from future analyses.

Palmieri's small angle data at 147 mev, and that of Fischer and Chamberlain at 300 mev, only give *relative* values of differential

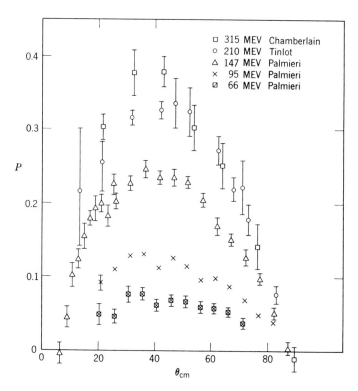

Figure 5-6. *P* versus θ for 66 to 315 mev *p-p* scattering.

cross sections at small angles. Although the authors normalized this data by hand, in any least squares adjustment of the data to a theory should be one of the adjustable constants. In particular Palmieri normalized his small angle data too high, and Chamberlain too low, as can be seen by comparison with neighboring angles. Figure 5-3 corrects this normalization.

5.3 Polarization Measurements

The polarization measurements are easier to make than the differential cross section measurements. For not only are the measurements relative, but the scattered energy does not change as the angle is changed from $+\theta$ to $-\theta$ so that absorber corrections remain the same and background corrections are similar. Measure-

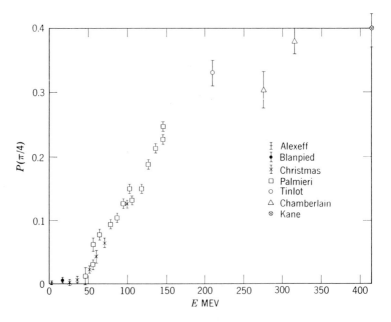

Figure 5-7. $P_{45°}$ versus E.

ments so far have all been made with beams polarized by scattering. This leaves a gap in direct beams from 20 to 140 mev. This gap has been filled by slowing down the protons with absorbers. The beam intensity is high so that precise measurements can be, and have been, obtained. The polarization of the incident beam has been measured in terms of carbon scattering. The apparatus is similar to or the same as that used for the differential cross section measurements. In Figure 5-6 are shown some plots of polarization versus angle at different energies, and in Figure 5-7 a plot of polarization versus energy at 45° cm.

All measurements are summarized in Table 5-3. The absolute

TABLE 5-3   POLARIZATION MEASUREMENTS

Author	Energy mev	Angular Range (cm)	Absolute Precision %	Relative Precision %	Polarization of Beam %
Alexeff (1960) Minnesota	3.1–3.5	30°–50°	0.2	0.2	40 94 [a]
Blanpied (1959) Princeton	18	50°	0.5	0.5	40
Batty (1962) Harwell	50	45°, 90°	3	0.2	30
Christmas (1961) Harwell	27–97	45°, 60°, 75°	5	0.5	45
Palmieri (1958) Harvard	40–147	45°		1	70
	66, 95, 118, 147	6°–90°	4	1	
Taylor (1959) Harwell	147, 95	10°–90°	3	2	45
Tinlot (1961) Rochester	210	30°–90°	2	1	90
Chamberlain (1957) Berkeley	276	20°–90°	6	3	67
	315	20°–90°	4	3	76
Kane (1954) Carnegie	415	15°–90°	10	2	45
Mescheriakov (1957) Dubna	635	12°–90°	5	2	58
Homer (1962) Birmingham	970	12°–81°	—	6	~35
Bareyre (1961) Saclay	2,000	10°–100°	5	5	50

[a] Analysing efficiency; asymmetry is measured.

precision is the precision with which the polarization of the beam is known, and *multiplies* all numbers. For small polarizations its effect is small. The relative precision is the precision arising from the asymmetry measurement itself.

5.4   Triple Scattering Measurements

In all the measurements, so far, of the Wolfenstein parameters D, R, A, R', the measurement has involved three scatterings. The first and third (polarizing and analysing) scatters have been on a nucleus, both to obtain a high polarizing (or analysing) power, and a high scattering cross section. A typical apparatus for the measurement of D is in Figure 5-8. This apparatus is that used at Har-

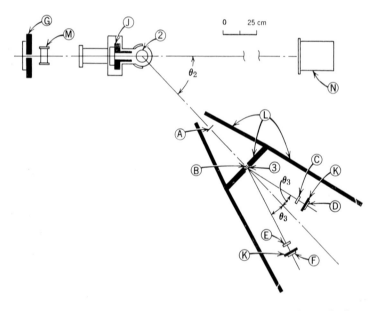

Figure 5-8. Apparatus for measurement of D at Harvard: (2) hydrogen target, (3) analyzing scatterer, (A–F) scintillation counters, (G) main slits, (J) antiscattering slits, (K) copper absorbers, (L) iron shielding, (M) ion chamber, and (N) Faraday cup.

vard. The incident beam has a polarization perpendicular to the paper, and is scattered in the plane of the paper by a liquid hydrogen target. Counters A and B define a scattered beam. After a third scattering by a carbon analyser, the protons are detected by one of two telescopes CD or EF. Shielding is so placed that a coincidence $ABCD$ is impossible without a scattering and absorber is used to reduce the background. The asymmetry at the third scatterer must be measured relative to a center line. The center line is defined by the center of counter B and the intersection of the beam line and the hydrogen target. This is a somewhat indefinite line. At Harvard it was determined by moving the counters CD and EF through the second scattered beam. Figure 5-9 shows a typical profile thus obtained. It is easy to find the center of gravity of this profile to 0.05°. The line can change with cyclotron operating con-

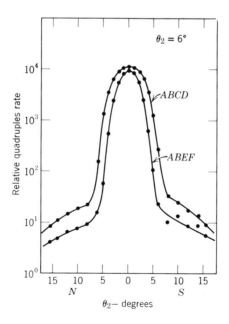

Figure 5-9. Profile of the twice scattered beam used to find the zero of the 3rd scattering angle θ_3.

ditions or with movement of the target, leading to serious misalign-
ment errors. The simple procedure outlined above enables the
alignment to be checked frequently. This procedure was followed
at Berkeley and Harvard.

It is also possible to measure the incident polarized beam direction (by a photographic film or an auxiliary counter) and thus
determine the scattered beam line by surveying. This procedure
was adopted at Rochester and Harwell and by Harvard as a check.

Both Harwell and Harvard use a solenoid to change the spin
direction. This enables the spin direction to be rapidly reversed,
and the asymmetry obtained. It is important to realize, however,
that with protons all problems are not thereby solved. In general
the solenoid also changes the beam direction and hence the alignment. The primary alignment errors are eliminated by so position-
ing the solenoid that the centroid of the beam at the target does
not change upon spin reversal. This is possible, except for small

TABLE 5-4   TRIPLE SCATTERING MEASUREMENTS

Authors	Energy mev	Angular θ_{cm}	Parameter	Solenoid	Alignment
Griffith (1963) London and Harwell	50	70°	D	Yes	{Split ion chamber
Thorndike (1960) Harvard	95	22°–62°	D	No	Counter
Hwang (1960) Harvard	140	12°–82°	D	No	Counter, film
Thorndike (1960) Hee (1963) Harvard	140	31°–82°	R, A, R'	Yes	Counter
Bird (1960, 1961) Jarvis (1962) Harwell	143	31°–90°	D, R, A	Yes	Film
Gotow (1962) Lobkowitz (1962) England (1961) Rochester	210	31°–90°	D, R, A, R'	No	{Film and subsidiary counter
Chamberlain (1957) Berkeley	310	31°–90°	D, R	No	Counter
Simmons (1956) Berkeley	310	25°–75°	A	No	Counter
Kumekin (1958, 1962) Dubna	660	40°–120°	D, R	No	

changes in the average beam direction with cyclotron operating
conditions. Systematic errors are further avoided by measuring at
both positive and negative analyzing angles simultaneously, and
at both positive and negative second scattering angles simultaneously. The change of position on solenoid reversal is measured at
Harwell by the blackening of a photographic film, at Harvard by
the more direct alignment procedure previously outlined. Either
should be adequate, though the film procedure could conceivably
give trouble in the unlikely event the beam contained large unused
and unwanted low-energy components.

The measurement of R and A are similar except that the appara-

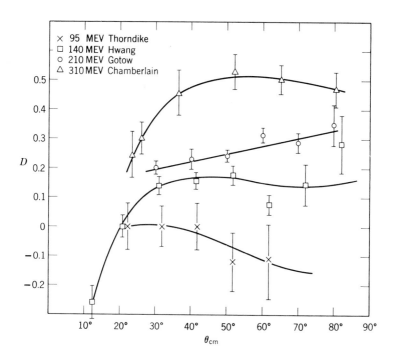

Figure 5-10. D for 95 to 310 mev p-p scattering. The lines are merely to guide
the eye.

tus and/or spin of the proton must be rotated through 90° for the R measurement. For the A measurement a magnet is necessary for rotating the polarization of the incident beam into the direction of motion.

R' is a little different, because now it is necessary to analyse longitudinal polarization after scattering, and a magnet is needed between the second and third scatterings. The difficulty arises in preventing spurious effects from the scattering of protons from the pole tips of a magnet placed between counters A and B, while simultaneously maintaining a reasonable solid angle.

As the angle of the second scattering θ is increased, the laboratory energy of the scattered proton falls. Also, the variation of energy with angle increases. Thus the proton does not easily escape

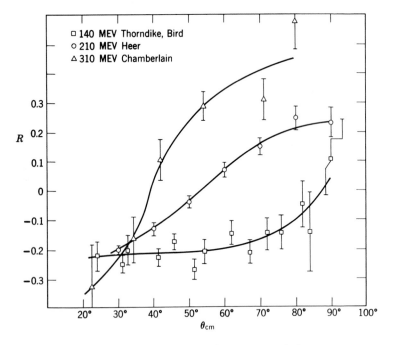

Figure 5-11. R for 140 to 310 mev p-p scattering.

from the target, and the angular resolution must also be improved. It is hard, therefore, to measure at large angles.

A worse problem is that the analyser efficiency decreases as the energy falls (see Figure 10-7) and is about 0.1 at 60 mev. This is also of course the trend of nucleon-nucleon polarization, and this decrease of efficiency can be explained in terms of the theory in Chapter 10. However, at lower energies (<20 mev) the efficiency can rise again where the scattering from nuclei is not given so simply in terms of nucleon-nucleon scattering.

The diminishing accuracy of the data as θ increases is seen in the data of Table 5-4. The upper angular limit is set entirely by the requirement of a finite analyzing power.

D, R, and A are plotted for different energies in Figures 5-10–5-12, and listed in Table 5-4.

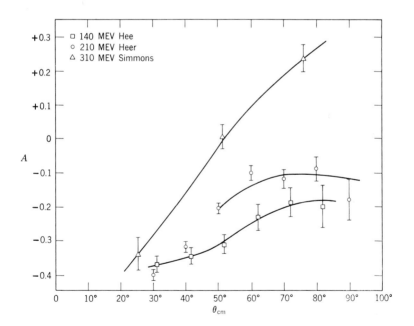

Figure 5-12. A from 140 to 310 mev for p-p scattering.

5.5   Correlation Parameters

Not much data is available on correlation parameters as yet.
Apparatus for measurement of the correlation parameter C_{nn} is
shown in Figure 5-13. The two protons from the pp scattering are

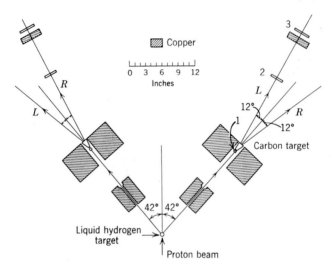

Figure 5-13. Apparatus for measuring p-p correlation parameter (Ashmore).

detected in coincidence, and each is scattered again in an analysing
scattering. The analysers are calibrated at a different time in a
polarized proton beam. The correlation parameter C_{nn} is given by

$$C_{nn}/P^2 = \frac{C_{LL} + C_{RR} - C_{RL} - C_{LR}}{C_{LL} + C_{RR} + C_{RL} + C_{LR}} \qquad (5\text{-}2)$$

where $C_{LL(RR)}$ represents the counts where each proton scatters
to the left (right) and P is the analyser efficiency. A rotation of one
analyzer through $90°$ gives C_{qp}.

The major problems with this experiment were random coincidences between the two telescopes caused primarily by a large neutron background. The beam intensity was reduced to enable this to be kept under control. The recent improvements in duty cycle (Chapter 4) would allow an increase of counting rate of a factor of 10–30 with consequent improved precision. In the Liverpool

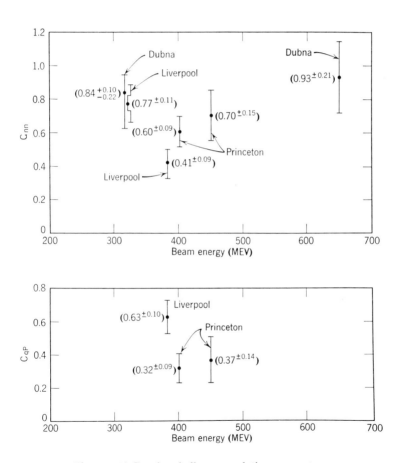

Figure 5-14. Results of all *p-p* correlation parameters.

measurements, only one telescope on each side was used so that to evaluate (5-2) four separate runs must be used and normalized.

It is possible to check the alignment of each telescope by examining the uncorrelated asymmetry, which should be zero.

The random background may be reduced by placing an anticoincidence counter in each telescope, so that a particle which triggers the first two counters, but does not scatter, is inhibited from forming a random coincidence with a neutron produced count in the second two.

These improvements are included in the work of Engels, who also introduced a spark chamber in each telescope to observe the

TABLE 5-5 CORRELATION PARAMETERS

Authors	Energy mev	Angle cm	Parameter	C
Abragam (1962) Saclay	20	90°	C_{nn}	-0.91 ± 0.05
Nisimura (1963) Tokyo	52.3	90°	C_{qp}	0.10 ± 0.14
Allaby (1961) Liverpool	310	90°	C_{nn}	0.77 ± 0.11
Vasilevsky (1961) Dubna	310	90°	C_{nn}	$0.84 \begin{cases} +0.10 \\ -0.22 \end{cases}$
Allaby (1961) Liverpool	350	90°	C_{nn}	0.41 ± 0.09
	350	90°	C_{qp}	0.63 ± 0.10
Allaby (1961) Liverpool	380	30°	C_{qp}	0.12 ± 0.10
	380	30°	C_{nn}	0.20 ± 0.10
Engels (1963) Chicago	400	90°	C_{nn}	0.60 ± 0.09
			C_{qp}	0.32 ± 0.09
	450	90°	C_{nn}	0.70 ± 0.15
			C_{qp}	0.37 ± 0.14
Golovin (1962) Dubna	650	90°	C_{nn}	0.93 ± 0.20
Nikanorov (1961) Dubna	660	90°	C_{qp}	$0.22 + 0.18$

scatterings. It is thus possible for him to measure C_{nn} and C_{qp} simultaneously. A further check is possible by verifying that the correlation of a scattering event on one side with the *previous* event on the other is zero. Five thousand pictures were analyzed. The spark chamber seems quite suited for this measurement if high accuracy is not required. To compete with the counter experiments listed in Table 5-4 where 40,000 events per angle are analyzed automatic data processing would be needed.

Table 5-5 and Figure 5-14 show the experimental results. The agreement between the experiments is not good. The errors, however, are still large, so that in a phase shift analysis, the correlation parameters do not have a great weight.

Chapter 6

Neutron Measurements

6.1 Total Cross Section

This is a much simpler measurement than the corresponding one for protons because there is no slowing down by atomic collisions. Neutrons from the cyclotron are collimated and pass to an energy measuring detector. Absorbers of CH_2 and C with the same number of C atoms per unit area are placed alternately in the beam. The comparison of counting rates gives the hydrogen cross section. Care must be taken about efficiency changes with count rate, multiple scattering and backgrounds. The detector may be a CH_2 target and telescope which measures energy by the range of a proton recoil or time of flight. For higher energies, where neutron beams are rarer, a $pd - pp$ subtraction is often used. As with the proton measurements, an integrated cross section from about 1° to 180° is measured. The Coulomb effects due to the magnetic moment all lie between 0 and 1°.

Figures 6-1 and 6-2 show σE and σ vs. E and Table 6-1 shows the measurements available.

6.2 Differential Cross Section Measurements

There are two regions for these; firstly that in which the proton recoil is detected (60°–180° cm) and secondly that in which the scattered neutron is detected (5°–90° cm). Problems arise from the broad neutron spectrum used and the variation of neutron de-

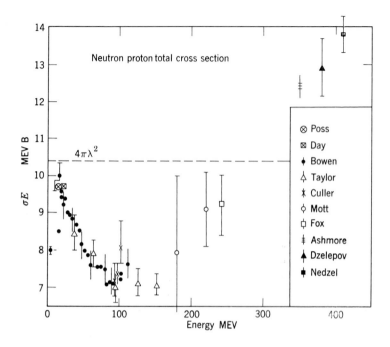

Figure 6-1. σE versus E for total np cross section.

tector efficiency with energy. The scattered neutron or recoil proton energy varies with angle as $E \cos^2 \theta$ (nonrelativistically), where θ is the lab angle. Above $\theta = 30°$ lab ($>60°$ cm) for neutron detection and above $30°$ lab (below $120°$ cm) for proton detection the variation is rapid. Indeed below $50°$ cm the variation in proton energy is so rapid and the energy is so small that proton detection in counters is not possible. Proton detection in cloud chambers and photographic plates has been attempted below $50°$ cm but the systematic errors make the results highly dubious, and they often disagree with neutron measurements.

The neutron spectra used usually have a sharp high-energy cutoff (the cyclotron energy) and the detector provides a low-energy cutoff. When the proton is detected, an absorber may define the minimum proton range and hence minimum neutron energy. This absorber must be changed as the angle is changed to refer to a constant incident neutron energy. For neutron detection, the detector may be a large liquid scintillator (Voss, 1954). The neutron is detected by a proton recoil from np scattering in the scintillator material. The allowable angular range of proton recoils and hence the efficiency is defined by the minimum allowable pulse height in the scintillator; the minimum neutron energy is also so detected. Coupling of detector efficiency and energy threshold requires a broad band of neutron energies to avoid uncertainty in the efficiency.

Alternatively a bank of scintillators in coincidence may be used (Miller, 1960), where the angular range of the proton recoil is de-

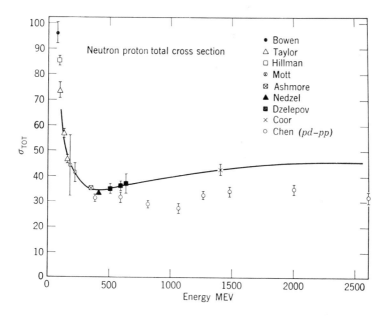

Figure 6-2. σ versus E for total np cross section.

TABLE 6-1 *np* TOTAL CROSS SECTIONS

Author	Energy (mev)	(Energy) Accuracy %	Method of E Measurement	σ (Accuracy) % Comment
Day (1953) Los Alamos	19.7	0.2	Source	0.6
Taylor (1952) Harwell	40–153	2	Range	2
Hillman (1954) Harvard	45, 88	2	Comparison	2
Bowen (1961) Harwell	20–111	2 (systematic)	Time of flight	2 (systematic)
Mott (1952) Rochester	100–190	2	Range	
Kazarinov (1962) Dubna	200	—	—	2
Ashmore (1957) Liverpool	350	1	Range	2
Nedzel (1954) Chicago	410	2	Range	4
Dzelephov (1955) Dubna	500–630	—	Range	6
Coor Brookhaven	1400	—	Range	5
Chen (1956) Brookhaven	600– 3 Bev	2	Magnet	10 (pd − pp) no correction for absorption

termined by the efficiency and the threshold by the range. This is more definite and stable than the first method but is less efficient.

When a neutron detector is used the normalization of the counts to give a differential cross section is direct. The counter is placed in the direct neutron beam. It is then set at the angle θ. The cross section is given by the ratio of the counts according to the formula

$$\sigma(\theta) = (\eta_0 C_\theta / \eta_\theta C_0) Nt\Omega \qquad (6\text{-}1)$$

where Nt is the number of atoms per gm cm^{-2} and Ω is the detection solid angle. The neutron detector efficiencies η_0 and η_θ cancel if there is no energy dependence. Only the Harwell measurements have been so normalized. The others (Carnegie, Dubna) are relative only.

When a proton detector is used, the data must be normalized to the total cross section by integration. This leads to uncertainty because of overlap with the region of the neutron measurements.

TABLE 6-2   *np* DIFFERENTIAL CROSS SECTION

Author	Energy	Angular Range	*p* or *n* Detection	Comment
Stahl (1954) Harvard	90 ± 2	$50°-180°$	p	
Bowen (1962) Harwell	$20-130$	$5°-180°$	p and n	Time of flight Absolute error n measurements 5%
Hobbie (1960) Harvard	128	$70°-160°$	p	
Voss (1955) Oxford and Harwell	137 ± 3	$5°-60°$	n	Absolute error 7%
Randle (1956) Harwell	133 ± 3	$30°-180°$	p	Cloud chamber
Randle (1952) Harwell	143 ± 3	$50°-180°$	p	
Kazarinov (1962) Dubna	200	$5°-180°$	p and n	
Easley (1954) Berkeley	90, 290	$10°-50°$	n	
DePangher (1955) Berkeley	300	$40°-180°$	p	Cloud chamber. Small angle points dubious
Kelly (1950) Berkeley	270	$50°-180°$	p	
Hartzler (1954) Carnegie	350	$15°-180°$	p and n	
Golovin (1958) Dubna	580	$5°-35°$	n	
Kazarinov (1957) Dubna	580	$40°-180°$	p	
Amaglobeli (1959) Dubna	630	$10°-180°$	n and p	
Ashmore (1962) Liverpool	350	$150°-180°$	p	
Larsen (1960) Berkeley	700	$150°-180°$	p	
Martelli (1961) Birmingham	775 1,010	$90°$	p	Inelastic *pd*
Palevsky (1962) Brookhaven	2,049 2,850	$169°-180°$	p	

Recent Harwell measurements use time of flight to select neutron energies and hence define both the high-energy and low-energy cutoff. The problem of change of threshold becomes much less serious, since the threshold is now set very low.

In Table 6-2 are outlined the presently available measurements. Figure 6-3 shows some typical angular distributions. On these plots

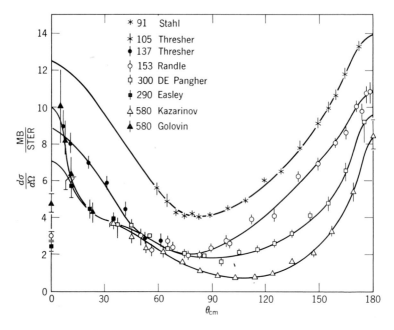

Figure 6-3. np angular distribution from 90 to 580 mev. The lines are merely to guide the eye.

the point at zero degrees is not real, but is $k^2 \sigma_{tot}^2/16\pi^2 = |\operatorname{Im} f(0)|^2$ and is a lower limit. The near symmetry about 90° at energies up to 90 mev is obvious.

No measurements have yet been made with a well defined neutron beam from $p(d, 2p)n$.

6.3   Polarization

Polarized neutrons have been used in similar experiments to the differential cross section measurements. No problem with the change in detector efficiency with angle arises. When the neutron polarization is low, it is particularly advantageous to use a magnet to reverse the spin direction and avoid changing geometry and background. Since the neutron has no charge, the change in direction of the neutron beam is necessarily zero on reversing the magnet.

Some of the measurements quoted use the quasielastic p-d scat-

TABLE 6-3 np POLARIZATION MEASUREMENTS

Author	Polarization of Beam	Energy mev	Max Polarization %	Solenoid	Comments
Benenson (1962) Wisconsin	-43%	16.4	4	Yes	free np
Benenson (1962) Wisconsin	$+46\%$	23.7	4	Yes	free np
Perkins (1963) Los Alamos	—	23.1	5	Yes	free np
Bowen (1961) Harwell	14%–30%	20–100	4–45	Yes	free np
Whitehead (1960) Harwell	25%	77	45	Yes	free np
Stafford (1957) Harwell	9%	95	45	Yes	free np
Hobbie (1960) Harvard	47%	128	50	No	free np
Stafford (1962) CERN	23%	140	50	Yes	free np
Kuckes (1961) Harvard	70%	143	50	No	quasielastic p-d
Tinlot (1961) Rochester	90%	208	50	No	quasielastic p-d
Chamberlain (1957) Berkeley	60%	310	45	No	quasielastic p-d
Siegel (1956) Carnegie	30%	350	40	No	free np
Golovin (1959) Dubna	—	635	25	No	quasielastic p-d

tering and a coincidence method; the theoretical errors are quite small. Some measurements at 310 and 600 mev using neutron detection only may have larger errors of interpretation.

At first sight one might argue that the quasielastic scattering measurements are far less accurate than the pure elastic scattering, because of the theoretical difficulties outlined in Chapter 3. A detailed comparison of the errors shows that this is not so.

There is a distribution of struck particle momenta ($\sim$15 mev) in the quasielastic scattering and an uncertainty of 1% in the effective energy. This corresponds to a distribution of incident neutron energies ($\sim$20 mev) and an uncertainty perhaps 2% of average. There is an uncertainty of final state corrections (<0.02) for quasielastic polarization. For pure elastic scattering there is a 10% un-

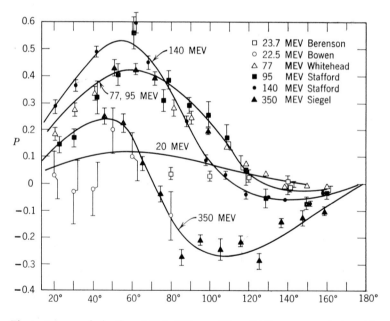

Figure 6-4. np polarization at 23 to 350 mev. The solid lines are merely to guide the eye.

certainty in beam polarization. We thus see that each type of experiment has its own type of error and neither excludes the other from consideration.

Figure 6-4 shows some polarization results. We wish to emphasize the complete agreement (at 140 mev and at 310–350 mev) between experiments using free np scattering and pd inelastic scattering. This agreement would not be found if there was a term $D(\sigma_{1n} - \sigma_{2n})$ in the scattering matrix [equation (3-6)]. It is therefore a test of charge symmetry additional to those in Chapter 9. As we shall see in Chapter 7, this term is the only term causing singlet/triplet mixing. Also the agreement confirms the use of the impulse approximation discussed in Chapter 3.

6.4 Triple Scattering

The first triple scattering parameters for free np scattering have been performed. The procedure is the same as for pp scattering. Figure 6-5 shows the apparatus. The recoil proton is studied. The reason for this choice is the desire to analyze a charged particle, and also the choice of angles is dictated by the necessity of finite energy of the recoil particle so that the analyzing power may be large.

TABLE 6-4 np TRIPLE SCATTERING MEASUREMENTS

Author	Energy (mev)	Angle cm	Param- eter	Solenoid	Comments
Patel (1962) Harvard	128	120°–160°	D_t	Yes	Free np
Hoffman (1962) Harvard	137	41°–82°	R, A	Yes	pd quasielastic
Warner (1962) Rochester	208	41°–90°	D	No	pd quasielastic, no checks on pp
Fischer (1957) Berkeley	310	41°–90°	D, R	No	pd quasielastic low precision

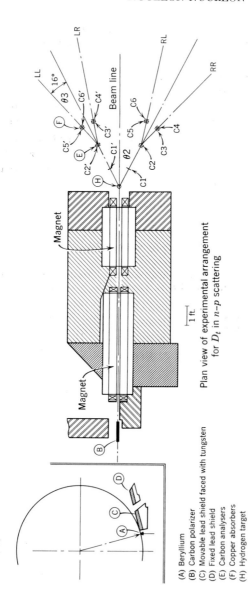

Figure 6-5. Apparatus for measuring the np triple scattering parameter D_t.

(A) Beryllium
(B) Carbon polarizer
(C) Movable lead shield faced with tungsten
(D) Fixed lead shield
(E) Carbon analysers
(F) Copper absorbers
(H) Hydrogen target

Plan view of experimental arrangement
for D_t in n-p scattering

In the case shown in the drawing, the polarization is analyzed perpendicular to the scattering plane. The incident polarization may be reversed by means of the precession magnets. The experiment is therefore D_t, where t indicates that it is the target (recoil) particle which is analyzed.

Another series of triple scattering experiments uses inelastic scattering from the deuteron, with a neutron coincidence. Again the high-energy proton is analyzed. A check is usually made by studying pp polarization from the quasielastic pd collisions with the same apparatus. The results have agreed, as expected, with the free pp triple scattering parameters. Table 6-4 summarizes available data, and Figures 6-6 to 6-8 plot them.

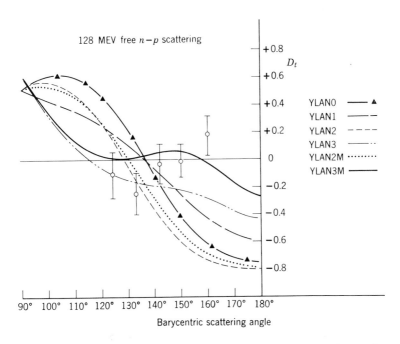

Figure 6-6. The parameter D_t at 128 mev. The lines are fits to data to be described in Chapter 7. Note the good fit to YLAN3M.

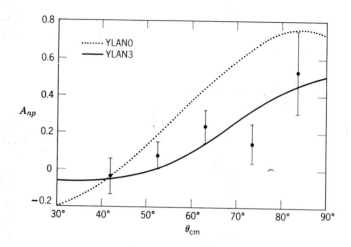

Figure 6-7. The parameter A in pn scattering at 135 mev. The lines are fits to be described in Chapter 7. Note the good fit to YLAN3. YLAN3M is close to this.

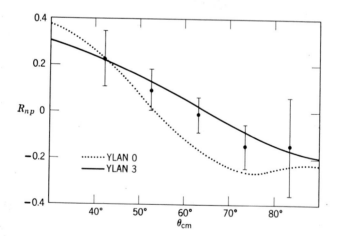

Figure 6-8. The parameter R in pn scattering at 137 mev. The lines are fits to be described in Chapter 7. Note the good fit to YLAN3. YLAN3M is close to this.

Theoretical Interpretation

7.1 Qualitative Information

a. Exchange Forces

High-energy scattering immediately tells us some important features of the nucleon-nucleon interaction. We noted that the effective range theory of low-energy interactions in Chapter 2 is identical whether we have an ordinary potential to describe the scattering or an exchange potential. The difference did not arise in S wave scattering. At high energies the scattering from an ordinary potential will peak predominantly in the forward direction and that from an exchange potential in the backward direction. This we see at once from the scattering amplitude in the first Born approximation

$$f(\theta, \Phi) = -\frac{1}{4\pi} \int \exp\left(i\mathbf{k}_0 \cdot \frac{\mathbf{r}_p - \mathbf{r}_n}{2}\right)$$
$$\times V(\mathbf{r}_p - \mathbf{r}_n) \exp\left(i\mathbf{k} \cdot \frac{\mathbf{r}_p - \mathbf{r}_n}{2}\right) d\mathbf{r} \quad (7\text{-}1)$$

for an ordinary potential $V(\mathbf{r}_p - \mathbf{r}_n)$ acting between the proton with position vector $\mathbf{r}_p$ and neutron $\mathbf{r}_n$. An exchange potential has the same form but interchanges $\mathbf{r}_p$ and $\mathbf{r}_n$ in the second expotential. The integral is only finite when $(\mathbf{k}_0 \pm \mathbf{k}).(\mathbf{r}_p - \mathbf{r}_n)$ is small where the negative sign is for ordinary and the positive for exchange

forces. Thus at high energies there is a peak near 180° cm angle
for exchange forces. Even for pure exchange forces, a small peak
at 0° is expected due to diffraction scatterings. Such scattering
would give peaks at both 0° and 180°. This suggested to Serber that
a mixture of half ordinary, half exchange forces, might be a good
first approximation. With this mixture the polarization is antisymmetric about 90°. This is not quite true and (Fig. 6-4) shows
that additional terms are certainly required. To the extent that
the "Serber mixture" is dominant in the np interaction the p
phases will be anomalously small and the effective range theory
which deals with S states alone, anomalously useful.

For pp scattering there is a symmetry about 90° due to the particle identity. This effect of exchange forces can thus only be seen
in the np system and $T = 0$ states. The angular distribution
(Fig. 6-3) of np scattering cross section up to 90 mev is remark-
ably symmetrical about 90° and has large peaks at 0° and 180°.

This 180° cm scattering peak shows up clearly at 2 and 3 Bev
(Palevsky, 1962). It cannot be due to exchange of a single π meson
because this vanishes at 0° and 180° due to the pseudoscalar
character of the meson. It may be due to a pair of π mesons or a ρ
meson or else an interference effect.

b. One Pion Exchange Potential

Scattering near 0° and 180° may be due to one pion exchange.
According to the present ideas, the potential is largely caused by
one pion exchange at large distances and small momentum transfers. The scattering amplitude from the one pion exchange term
has poles at an angle given by $\cos \theta = \pm(1 + \mu/M)$ where μ and M
are the masses of the pion and nucleon, respectively. At these
poles the scattering is given exactly by meson theory. The scattering in the region of these poles is then dominated by the pole
scattering. The experimental data is then extrapolated to the
pole—with some plausible extrapolation function—to yield the
pion nucleon coupling constant. This procedure may be followed
both near 0° and near 180° and may, in principle, be applied to pp
cattering near 0°. In the latter case, Coulomb interference domi-

nates; we note however that we may extrapolate any combination of experimental amplitudes that does not contain A or C, of equation (3-6)—the only amplitudes with Coulomb terms. By examining Table 3-2 we see that $\sigma(1 - D) = \frac{1}{2}(G^2 + H^2)$ is such a combination.

Some extrapolations are summarized in Table 7-1. We would

TABLE 7-1 PION-NUCLEON COUPLING CONSTANT
BY EXTRAPOLATION

Author	Energy	Order of Extrapolation Polynomial	Angular Range	f^2
Thorndike (1962)	142	$\sigma(1 - D)\ pp$		0.05 ± 0.01
Kazarinov (1961)	147–380	pp		0.07 ± 0.015
Amaglobeli (1960)	90			0.06 ± 0.006
Amaglobeli (1960)	380			0.065 ± 0.007
Amaglobeli (1960)	630			0.044 ± 0.012
Ashmore (1962)	350	several	150°–180°	0.079 ± 0.005
Larsen (1960)	710	3	158°–180°	0.059 ± 0.022
Larsen (1960)	710	+ "pseudo pole"		0.085 ± 0.011
Cziffra (1959)	90	3	129°–180°	0.062 ± 0.02
Cziffra (1959)	90	6	5.1°–180°	0.065 ± 0.02
Cziffra (1959)	400	5	90°–180°	0.066 ± 0.01
Cziffra (1959)	400	5	12.7°–180°	0.059 ± 0.007
Value from pion-nucleon scattering				0.081
Value from boundary condition fit				0.0856 ± 0.002

like to emphasize that the choice of extrapolation function involves assumptions. The use of a pole contribution is inherent in the use of a phase shift analysis. Other values for the coupling constant are derivable from the phase shift analyses (Breit, 1960, 1962; Table 7-3, page 119).

110   NUCLEON-NUCLEON INTERACTION

c. Hard Core

If the potential between two nucleons, $V(r_p - r_n)$, were a monatonic function of $(r_p - r_n)$ we would expect the phases to increase monatonically with energy. Then, from equation (2-12)

$$\sigma E = \sum_{l=0}^{\infty} (2l + 1) \sin^2 \delta_l \qquad (7\text{-}2)$$

would also increase monatonically. Yet Figure 5-1 and Figure 6-1 show that σE *falls* between 10 and 80 mev, where (7-2) is dominated by the S-wave interaction. The more detailed phase shift analyses show that the S phases are in fact falling, and become negative about 200 mev. This has been attributed to the presence of a hard (repulsive) core in the potential. At long wavelengths some sort of average of the potential is felt; at shorter wavelengths the hard core scatters with a negative amplitude and cancels the attractive scattering of the outer region. This effect, of course, occurs first for the S phase, and at shorter wavelengths for high momentum phases too. Care must be taken not to attach too much reality to this core. Similar effects can occur for a model with an energy independent boundary condition, and maybe it is all a relativistic correction anyway.

7.2   Phase Shift Analyses

In practice an attempt to analyze the data directly in terms of the scattering matrix 3-6 with the aid of the equation (3-7) is full of difficulty, and has not been done. An alternative procedure is to proceed via the phase shift expansion discussed in 2. The interaction must now include, in general, spin dependent effects. l is no longer a good quantum number as assumed in equation (2-12).

A detailed discussion is not possible here. We follow briefly the treatment of Blatt (1952). It is important to realize that only the square of the total angular momentum vector $\mathbf{J} = \mathbf{L} + \mathbf{S}$ and its z component J_z are constants of the motion, and therefore only the quantum numbers J and J_z can be used to specify states of the system. We also note that states with even L have even parity and with odd L odd parity and do not mix for parity conserving interactions.

We thus find that we can define a unique phase shift for triplet states with $L = J$, but we must define a nondiagonal matrix to relate amplitudes of the states $L = J + 1$ after collision to those before. There are now three constants required, the phases $\delta_{J,J+1}$ and $\delta_{J,J-1}$ and a coupling parameter ϵ_J.

The usual form of the matrix is

$$S = \begin{pmatrix} \bar{\delta}_{J,J+1} & 0 \\ 0 & \bar{\delta}_{J,J-1} \end{pmatrix} \begin{pmatrix} \cos 2\,\bar{\epsilon}_J & \sin 2\,\epsilon_J \\ -\sin 2\,\bar{\epsilon}_J & \cos 2\,\epsilon_J \end{pmatrix}$$

$$\times \begin{pmatrix} \bar{\delta}_{J,J+1} & 0 \\ 0 & \delta_{J,J-1} \end{pmatrix} \quad (7\text{-}3)$$

where the phases are called the nuclear bar phases to distinguish them from a slightly different parameterization of Blatt and Biedenharn. This matrix is obviously unitary, which is necessary to satisfy particle conservation. The parameterization of Blatt and Biedenharn (1952) is

$$S = \begin{pmatrix} \cos \epsilon_J & \sin \epsilon_J \\ -\sin \epsilon_J & \cos \epsilon_J \end{pmatrix} \begin{pmatrix} \delta_{J,J+1} & 0 \\ 0 & \delta_{J,J-1} \end{pmatrix} \begin{pmatrix} \cos \epsilon_J & \sin \epsilon_J \\ -\sin \epsilon_J & \cos \epsilon_J \end{pmatrix}$$

$$(7\text{-}4)$$

The phases $\delta_{J,J+1}$, $\delta_{J,J-1}$ are usually called loosely the phases in the states $L = J \pm 1$. They are only strictly phases in these states in the limit of no mixing $\epsilon_J = 0$.

Coulomb effects are accounted for by a WKB model in the outer region, making

$$S_{\text{tot}} = C S_{\text{nucl.}} C \quad (7\text{-}5)$$

where

$$C = \begin{pmatrix} e^{2i\phi_{J+1}} & 0 \\ 0 & e^{2i\phi_{J-1}} \end{pmatrix} \quad (7\text{-}6)$$

and $\phi_{J\pm1}$ is the Coulomb phase shift. It is then clear that in the first (bar) representation the Coulomb and nuclear phases add directly. The structure of this formula becomes physically clear when we realize that the WKB approximation implies that the trajectory of the nucleon is well defined in the scattering region. It then becomes possible to directly *add* the phase changes along this trajectory. The phases in this second representation are called bar phases as opposed to BB phases, and are now always used. There is only a difference in the mixed phases.

The spins of the two nucleons can combine into four possible combinations which are conveniently grouped into triplet and singlet spin states. For each orbital angular momentum L these may be three values of $J = L \pm 1$, L for triplet states, and $J = L$ for singlet states.

Now we remark on the symmetry on the interchange of the two nucleons spin triplet ($S = 1$) and orbital angular momentum functions of even L are symmetric under exchange, and spin singlet ($S = 0$) and odd L are antisymmetric. The Pauli exclusion principle states that for a system of identical particles (pp or nn) the total wavefunction must be antisymmetric. Thus for the pp system even L states must be spin singlet and odd L spin triplet. For the np case there is no such restriction, but it is convenient to consider the neutron and proton as identical particles in different states of isotopic spin T with $T_z = -\frac{1}{2}$ and $+\frac{1}{2}$, respectively. The Pauli principle now applies, and the pp system only appears in $T = 1$ states, and the np system in either $T = 0$ states.

We classify in Table 7-2 the states in spectroscopic notation in order of increasing L; the superscript indicates a triplet or singlet, and the subscript the value of J.

TABLE 7-2   CLASSIFICATION OF STATES OF
NUCLEON-NUCLEON SYSTEM
(Spectroscopic Notation)

$T\backslash L$	0	1	2	3	etc.
1	$^1S_0$	$^3P_{0,1,2}$	$^1D_2$	$^3F_{2,3,4}$	
0	$^3S_1$	$^1P_1$	$^3D_{1,2,3}$	$^1F_3$	

This classification does not prove that L, S or T are constants of the motion. $|\mathbf{J}|^2 = |\mathbf{L} + \mathbf{S}|^2$ and J_z are constants from invariance under rotation, but states of different L but the same J can couple. Now states of even L have even parity and odd L odd parity, so states of even and odd L do not mix unless parity conservation is violated. In particular we note that the ground state of the deuteron is a mixture of ^3S and ^3D components but no ^3P component; a ^3P component would give an electric dipole moment. Also in all situations we consider, the interaction is symmetric under interchange of the spin coordinates only showing S (but not S_2) is a good quantum number and that triplet and singlet states do not mix. Such a mixture would also mix $T = 0$ and $T = 1$ states.

Before we proceed we note that there exists an alternative representation in terms of helicity states (Jacob, 1959) in which different combinations appear. This representation is especially useful for electron scattering processes and for pion-nucleon scattering. Maybe it has utility here.

It is important to realize that phase shifts are not the aim and end of the study of nucleon-nucleon interaction. They are stepping stones—they summarize experimental data, and even then not as well as we would wish.

In order to carry out a phase shift analysis with an arbitrary number of phases, it is necessary to have experimental points at all angles; just as it is necessary for the use of equation (3-4). The question arises, how many angles constitute "all"? Experimentally it is easy to answer this question. It is necessary that measurements be taken at sufficiently small angular intervals that the parameters (cross section, polarization, etc.) may be found at any other angle by plausible interpolation. Theoretically this implies that there must not be too many nonzero phase shifts involved in the description of the scattering. The requirements of the unitarity equation (3-4) and of the phase shift analyses are the same.

It is important, when performing a phase shift analysis, to have an objective criterion for choosing how many phase shifts to include. Errors may creep in, and have in the past crept in, if this is not correctly done. For example if only S and P phases are included, the cross section will have the form

$$a + b \cos \theta + c \cos^2 \theta \qquad (7\text{-}7)$$

The parameter c is proportional to the square of the P phase shifts and b to the interference between the S and P phases. It would be tempting to use an experimental determination of the parameter c to help find the phase shifts, but this would be incorrect. If the D phase shift may be neglected, then the P phase shifts are already small. The parameter c has also contributions from the (neglected) SD interference which is probably of the same order as the square of the P phase shifts.

7.3   One Pion Exchange

A definite criterion for a cutoff of the number of phases has now been devised, which makes use of other information. The nuclear forces are expected to be due to the exchange of one or more mesons or other particles. The lightest known meson which interacts strongly is the π meson, and although it is yet possible that weakly interacting particles have been missed in searches for new particles, these would not enter into nuclear forces and no strongly interacting particle could have been missed.

The range of interaction corresponding to the interchange of n particles of mass m is, according to elementary theory, $\hbar/nmc$. The interaction of *longest* range is therefore due to the exchange of one particle of the lightest mass—the one pion exchange.

Now classically the interaction of particles of momentum $\mathbf{k}$ at a distance $\mathbf{r}$ is in a state of angular momentum $\mathbf{k} \times \mathbf{r}$. According to quantum mechanics, angular momentum is quantized in units of $\hbar$; the classical picture is still approximately valid if $\mathbf{k} \times \mathbf{r} \gg \hbar$. Under this picture, it is possible to relate each state of angular momentum L to a radius of interaction

$$r = L\hbar/k \qquad (7\text{-}8)$$

which formula is valid for large L. The quantitative validity of this is discussed by Breit (1962) following the first suggestion by Takerani and collaborators.

The considerations of the last two paragraphs may now be combined in the statement that the interaction in the states of largest angular momentum is given by the one pion exchange potential (OPEP), provided the angular momentum is large compared to unity. It may be further correctly argued that since the interaction in these angular momentum states is small, the first Born approximation is valid to calculate the effect of the OPEP. There is now a definite criterion of the way in which phase shifts of large angular momentum fall to zero. The one pion potential from meson theory is

$$V = \frac{1}{3}\, g^2 \left(\frac{h}{2Mc}\right)^2 (\boldsymbol{\tau}_1 \cdot \boldsymbol{\tau}_2) \left[(\boldsymbol{\sigma}_1 \cdot \boldsymbol{\sigma}_2) + S_{12}\left(1 + \frac{3}{\mu r} + \frac{3}{\mu^2 r^2}\right)\right] \frac{e^{-\mu r}}{r}$$

$$(7\text{-}9)$$

where $\mu = (m_\pi c/h)$.

The OPEP has been introduced here as a way of reducing the arbitrariness in the phase shift analyses. It is a quantitative question, to be answered only by the analyses themselves, which phase shifts are given by OPEP values and which are not. Thus an analysis might include SPDFG phases and higher phases from OPEP. If the G phases are close to the OPEP values, then it is clear that the analysis is validated. If, however, the G phases are significantly different from the OPEP values, it would probably not be valid to express the higher phases in the OPEP form. If the G phases were different from the OPEP values but not significantly so statistically, the data would be inadequate to confirm or reject the validity of the analysis. See Table 7-3 (page 119).

The one pion exchange has here been introduced as a method of reducing the arbitrariness in a phase shift analysis. It is related to the assumption of short range forces (based on nuclear binding energies) and the validity of the effective range theory. We, of course, wish to reduce theory to a minimum before we have completely summarized the data with the phase shifts. In calculating the OPEP terms two parameters enter—the pion-nucleon coupling constant (renormalized and obtained from pion-nucleon scattering) f and the meson mass (m_π). These can be used as adjustable parameters in a phase shift analysis. If the adjustment does not give the values of f and m_π known from other data, the approach is invalid. Although we have discussed the validity of OPEP using a potential and first Born approximation, the calculations have all employed a full covariant treatment.

At low energies, the use of OPEP can reduce the number of phases required to S and P (four phases) instead of the minimum of five parameters per angle of Chapter 3.

So far we have considered a separate phase shift analysis for each energy. There must clearly be some limitation on the complexity of the problem; again it can be said experimentally that it is necessary to perform experiments at energies such that it is possible to find the values of the parameters at any intermediate energy. Theoretically, a clear cut statement is hard to make. Considerations of causality give a maximum rate of change of phase shifts with energy; these considerations are probably not sufficiently restrictive.

Two approaches are possible. The first is to carry out phase shift analyses at each energy (310, 210, 147, 95, 68 mev) at which a considerable body of data exists and to draw smooth curves through plots of the phase shifts vs. energy. Small adjustments are necessary because the energies at which the data are taken are rarely exactly the same. Thus at Harvard, differential cross section measurements are available at 147 mev, whereas A and R' are measured at 139 mev.

The second method is to assume a plausible functional dependence for the phase shifts, given perhaps by meson theory, which has a suitable number of arbitrary constants, and to adjust to find the constants using data at all energies simultaneously. The one pion exchange would again, of course, be used. The problem here is to select the functional form without putting unreasonable constraint on the data. This second method, as first reported in 1959 and detailed by Breit (1960, 1962), gave the first unique set of phase shifts.

7.4 Proton-Proton Phase Shift Analysis Results

The results of the analyses at 140 and 210 mev show that there is only one acceptable solution. At 95 mev several are possible but only one has a positive D phase. At other energies more than one solution is possible but most may be excluded by the obvious requirement that the phase shifts be on a smooth curve as a function of energy. See Table 7-4 (page 122).

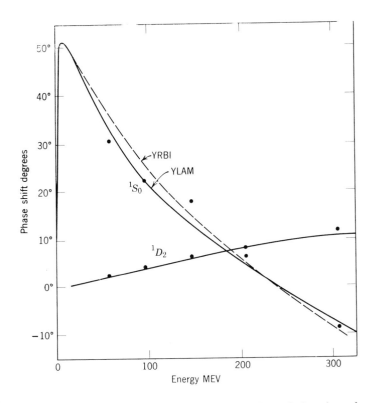

Figure 7-1. ^1S and ^1D phases versus energy from YLAM solution of pp phase shift search of Breit. Points are the solutions of Table 7-4.

The results for the S and P phases are presented in Figures 7-1 and 7-2. The curves are the results from an energy dependent phase shift search, and the points thereon are from the energy independent searches. Table 7-4 shows the numbers from energy independent

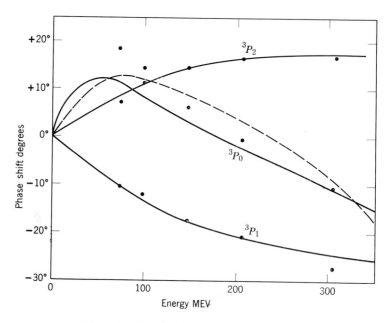

Figure 7-2. $^3P_0$, $^3P_1$, $^3P_2$ phases versus energy.

searches. The errors are defined as the change required to increase χ^2 by one unit. This is a *correlated* error. If the other phases were readjusted, a good fit might again be obtained. Because of the correlations, these numbers therefore *understate* the errors. This is the reverse of the usual way of counting errors in simpler problems and caution is therefore necessary. In practice it is best to use the whole error matrix. For this reason, the errors are *not* included in Table 7-4 (page 122).

TABLE 7-3 PHASE SHIFT $(T = 1)$ ANALYSES OF
pp-SCATTERING DATA [a]

Author	Energy	Data Used	States Used	OPEP
Noyes (1960)	68	σ, P	$^1S_0{}^3P_{0,1,2}{}^1D_2\epsilon_2$	Yes
Signell (1962)	95	σ, P, D $\sigma\ P\ D\ R\ A$	$^1S_0{}^3P_{0,1,2}{}^1D_2\epsilon_2$	Yes
Palmieri (1963)	147	$\sigma\ P\ D\ R\ A$		Yes
Signell (1962)	210	$\sigma\ P\ D\ R\ A\ R'$	$^1S_0{}^3P_{0,1,2}{}^1D_2\epsilon_2{}^3F_{2,3,4}$	Yes
Stapp Ypsilantis Metropolis (1957)	310	$\sigma\ P\ D\ R\ A$ $[P$ in π^+ production]	$^1S_0 \to {}^3H_0$	No
Cziffra (1959)	310	$\sigma\ P\ D\ R\ A$ $[P$ in π^+ production]	$^1S_0 \to {}^3F_4$	Yes
Gelfand (1960)	95, 150, 310	Unknown		Yes
Breit (1960)	$0 \to 310$ continuous	$\sigma\ P\ D\ R\ A$		Yes
Noyes (1960)	$0 \to 310$ continuous	$\sigma\ P\ D\ R\ A\ C$		Yes
MacGregor (1961)	9–98	$\sigma\ P$		Yes

[a] Unique $T = 1$ phase shift analyses have also been carried out at 52 mev by Hoshizaki (1963) and at 142 mev by Perring (1963).

7.5 Neutron-Proton Phase Shift Analysis

A complete phase shift analysis of np scattering has yet to be performed. The usual situation is to assume charge independence, and hence the $T = 1$ phases from pp scattering (Table 7-3). np cross section and polarization data then suffices for a solution.

MacGregor (1961) has completed such an analysis at 95 mev. Hull (1961) and Noyes (1960) have attempted an energy depend-ent analysis as has just been described for the pp system. Again, $T = 1$ phases are taken from the pp system. The starting points were not random sets, so that it is not entirely clear that all solutions have been found. It is noteworthy, however, that the phase shift sets *predicted* the values for R, A and D discussed in Chapter 6 which were not included in the search. In Figures 6-6, 6-7, and 6-8 the curve of the solution YLAN3M is plotted. This has $T = 1$ phases from solution YLAM (Breit, 1960). The other solutions may tentatively be rejected on the following grounds: the lack of fit to (1) D_t at 128 mev, (2) A at 135 mev, (3) the quadrupole moment of the deuteron, and, (4) np polarization near 20 mev.

The low angular momentum phases are plotted in Figures 7-3 and 7-4. The point on the curve is the phase shift analysis of Mac-

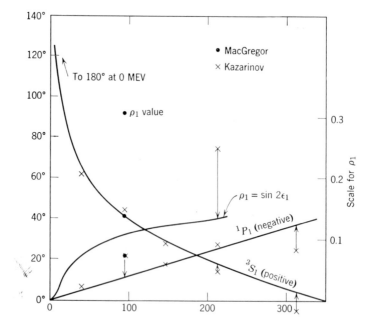

Figure 7-3. $^3S_1$, $^1P_1$, ϵ_1 phases versus energy. YLAM3M solution of np phase shift search of Hull 1961. Point of MacGregors's 12 parameter fit (1961), and of Kazarinov (1962).

Gregor. There seems to be agreement except for the $^1P_1$ phase. Note that the low-energy behaviour of ρ_1 is given by

$$\rho_1 = \sin 2\bar{\epsilon}_1 \simeq 2\bar{\epsilon}_1 \simeq 2\epsilon_1 \sin (\bar{\delta}_{0,1} - \bar{\delta}_{2,1})$$
$$\simeq 2Qk^2 \sin \delta_t \simeq Qk^3 \sqrt{(2\sigma_{\text{tot}}/\pi)}^{\,1/2} \quad (7\text{-}10)$$

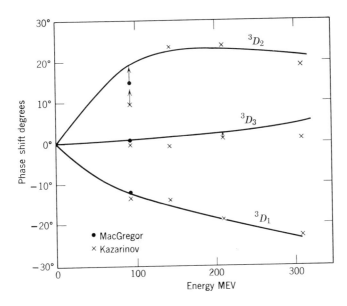

Figure 7-4. $^3D_1$, $^3D_2$, $^3D_3$ phases versus energy.

Kazarinov and Silin (1962) have recently carried out phase shift analyses at constant energy for both $T = 0$ and $T = 1$ phase shifts using both np and pp scattering data. They claim two solutions one of which gives $T = 1$ phases similar to those in Table 7-4. This is the only acceptable solution. The $T = 0$ phases are plotted on Figures 7-3 and 7-4. They do not include in their search the recent values of D_t, R, A in np and pn scattering near 130 mev or D near 210 mev although their phase shifts give results in general agree-

TABLE 7-4 pp $(T = 1)$ PHASE SHIFT SOLUTIONS
(Nuclear Bar Phases in Degrees)

Energy mev	$^1S_0$	$^1D_2$	$^3P_0$	$^3P_1$	$^3P_2$	ϵ_2	$^3F_2$	$^3F_3$	$^3F_4$	Higher Phases
68 [a,b]	30.5	2.6	18.6	−10.5	7.0	−2.4				OPEP
95 [a]	22.2	3.9	14.2	−12.0	11.2	−2.8				OPEP
147	17.7	5.7	7.6	−16.8	14.2	−5.0	−2.2	−0.7	0.25	OPEP
210	5.44	7.14	−0.032	−22.1	16.4	−2.78	−0.012	−2.39	1.21	OPEP
310	−8.9	11.9	−11.3	−27.5	16.6	−1.6	1.2	−3.5	3.5	OPEP

[a] Unique only if $^1D_2$ assumed positive.
[b] This solution is confirmed by recent C_{nn} and D measurements at 50 mev.

ment with the new data. Without this inclusion it is not quite clear why the solution should be more unique than that of the Yale group (Hull, 1962) who analyzed the same data. The solutions, however, are the plausible ones analogous to YLAN3M. The errors have not been included because of the correlations, but we note that ρ_1 is very badly determined, and at 40 mev the D phases are not determined. The source of the discrepancy between the groups at 95 mev in the $^3D_2$ and $^1P_1$ phases is not clear. The analysis of Perring (1963) gives similar phases to Kazarinov, but determines $\rho_1 = \sin 2\epsilon_1$ better because of inclusion of triple scattering data.

7.6 Validity of One Pion Exchange

The phase shift analyses confirm the validity of the one pion exchange for the long range part of the interaction. Thus χ^2 is a minimum at the correct meson mass (range) and at the correct (derived from pion nucleon data) coupling constant. Moreover the coupling constant is the same for np interactions as for pp interactions. Thus we can use the one pion exchange in other calculations. This has been already assumed for evaluating the fraction of D state from the quadrupole moment, and for theoretical values for the shape parameter P_t in Chapter 2. It will be shown in Chapter 8 how it can be used to discuss electron-deuteron interactions.

The most detailed extraction of the coupling constants f^2 from the one pion exchange contribution, both in pp and np scattering, is in Breit (1960, 1962). Even two pion exchange contributions are considered by Breit (1961).

7.7 Potential Models

Attempts have been made to describe the scattering by an energy independent potential. Such a potential must have the following features: (1) It must reduce to the one pion exchange potential at large distances. (2) It must have a repulsion at small distances to make the S phases reverse sign.

A third feature is the order of the ^3P and the ^3F phases in first Born approximation; the ^3F phase and at low energy the ^3P

phases have the ordering of the tensor force of the one pion exchange. Above 100 mev the ^3P phases change order (Fig. 7-3) showing that a new spin dependence enters. This is the spin orbit interaction. It is found to have a range of the order of the repulsive core. A longer range would give a larger $^3P_0$ phase and a negative value for D in pp scattering at 60° cm above 120 mev.

A potential derived by Hamada and Johnston (1962) to fit the data has been given in equation (7-11) where the parameters a, b are different in singlet even and odd and triplet even and odd states. The numerical values are listed in Table 7-5.

TABLE 7-5   VALUES OF THE PARAMETERS IN THE HAMADA-JOHNSTON POTENTIAL EQUATION (7-10)

State	Singlet Even	Triplet Even	Singlet Odd	Triplet Odd
a_c	+8.7	+6.0	−8.0	−9.07
b_c	+10.6	−1.0	+12.0	+3.48
a_T	—	−0.5	—	−1.29
b_T	—	+0.2	—	+0.55
G_{LS}	—	+0.074	—	+0.20
b_{LS}	—	−0.1	—	−7.1
ϵ_{LL}	−0.00089	+0.0027	−0.0027	−0.00089
a_{LL}	+0.2	+1.8	+2.0	−7.3
b_{LL}	−0.2	−0.4	+6.0	+6.9

No claim is made that this potential is unique, though all the four parts to $V(r)$ are necessary. The potential includes the one pion exchange part, a repulsive core, and both linear and quadratic spin orbit couplings. It should be useful for calculation of off energy shell effects (Chapter 8). Other potentials have been discussed by Bryan (1960) and Lassila (1962).

$$V(r) = V_C(r) + V_T(r)S_{12} + V_{LS}(r)(\mathbf{L} \cdot \mathbf{S}) + V_{LL}(r)L_{12}$$

$$L_{12} = (\boldsymbol{\sigma}_1 \cdot \boldsymbol{\sigma}_2)\mathbf{L}^2 - \tfrac{1}{2}[(\boldsymbol{\sigma}_1 \cdot \mathbf{L})(\boldsymbol{\sigma}_2 \cdot \mathbf{L}) + (\boldsymbol{\sigma}_2 \cdot \mathbf{L})(\boldsymbol{\sigma}_1 \cdot \mathbf{L})]$$

$$= \{\delta_{LJ} + (\boldsymbol{\sigma}_1 \cdot \boldsymbol{\sigma}_2)\}\mathbf{L}^2 - (\mathbf{L} \cdot \mathbf{S})^2$$

$$V_C = 0.08 \frac{\mu}{3} (\boldsymbol{\tau}_1 \cdot \boldsymbol{\tau}_2)(\boldsymbol{\sigma}_1 \cdot \boldsymbol{\sigma}_2) Y(x)[1 + a_c Y(x) + b_c Y(x)^2]$$

$$V_T = 0.08 \frac{\mu}{3} (\boldsymbol{\tau}_1 \cdot \boldsymbol{\tau}_2)(\boldsymbol{\sigma}_1 \cdot \boldsymbol{\sigma}_2) Z(x)[1 + a_T Y(x) + b_T Y^2(x)]$$

$$V_{LS} = \mu G_{LS} Y^2(x)[1 + b_{LS} Y(x)]$$

$$V_{LL} = \mu G_{LL} \frac{Z(x)}{x^2} [1 + a_{LL} Y(x) + b_{LL} Y^2(x)]$$

$$Y(x) = \exp(-x)/x$$

$$Z(x) = (1 + 3/x + 3/x^2) Y(x)$$

$$\mu = \text{pion mass} \qquad x = r\mu c/\hbar^2$$

Potential is infinite for

$$x \leq 0.343 \text{ (hard core)} \qquad (7\text{-}11)$$

7.8 Boundary Condition Models

It has been suggested by many authors, and Feshbach (1961) has stressed, that it is more sensible not to refer to the hard core and spin orbit potential, but to stop the potential at a distance r_0, and at $r = r_0$ to use an energy independent boundary condition for the wave function.

$$F = r_0 \left(\frac{1}{\chi} \frac{\partial \chi}{\partial r} \right) \qquad (7\text{-}12)$$

This condition must be different in each angular momentum state.

Outside this radius there is a potential described by one pion exchange and two pion exchange. There are two ambiguities about the latter—whether there is any pair suppression and whether Brueckner and Watson or the Japanese school have the correct method of calculation. Feshbach *et al.* treat these theoretical unknowns as adjustable constants together with the boundary conditions.

So far they have fitted the phase shifts at 90, 150, 210, and 310 mev as given by Breit *et al.* and the low energy data fit well. The constants are shown in Table 7-6. The ultimate aim is to reduce

TABLE 7-6   PARAMETERS OF BOUNDARY CONDITION MODEL ACCORDING TO FESHBACH'S ANALYSIS OF pp DATA

Phase	Jls	F	ΔF
$^1S_0$	000	1.08	0.05
$^1D_2$	220	3.14	1.
$^3P_0$	011	−7.82	1
$^3P_1$	111	13.37	6
$^3P_2$	211	−0.26	0.1
ϵ_2	$J = 2$ coupling	0.01	0.1
$^3F_2$	231	−4.06	0.05
$^3F_3$	331	−3.24	0.7

the whole of the pp results in this book to eight arbitrary constants, and this would certainly be a great step forward. These eight constants involve the interaction at small distances. Large F corresponds to a repulsive core. It is interesting that no repulsion appears in the $^1S_0$ state, in contrast to the qualitative picture given earlier. It suggests caution in referring to the results of the electron-deuteron scattering in Chapter 8.

7.9   Effects of Other Mesons

Breit (1937, 1959) and Sakurai (1959) suggested that a meson of spin 1 could explain both the repulsive core and the spin orbit coupling, two features of nucleon-nucleon potentials which are introduced *ad hoc*. In particular Sakurai observed that the parameter C in Wolfenstein's expression of the scattering matrix [equation (3-6)] is almost entirely imaginary corresponding to a first Born approximation calculation with a $J = 1$ particle, just as the one pion exchange gave a real amplitude A for 180° scattering. Two $J = 1$ mesons have since been discovered—the ρ meson with $T = 1$

decaying into two π mesons, and the ω meson with $T = 0$ and decaying into three π mesons. They appear to dominate electron-
nucleon scattering and have strong effects in pion nucleon scattering. Another, the η meson, has $T = 0$, $J = 0$; a meson with $T = 1$
is suggested. Whatever their spin they will contribute to nucleon-
nucleon scattering but the coupling constants are as yet unknown.
Amati (1959, 1960) and McKean (1962) suggest that they dominate
the short range part of the interaction, and render unnecessary any
consideration of uncorrelated two pion states. The work of Feshbach (1961) just described seems to be in contradiction to this and
suggests that the effects are contained in the logarithmic deriva-
tives F at a boundary, and have no effect at larger r. Two pion exchange may be correctly included *either* by a second-order perturba-
tion *or* by assuming a bound two pion state (ρ or ω).

The calculations of Amati use the helicity representation (Jacob,
1958). Electron-nucleon scattering can be used in this representation directly to give the meson-nucleon vertices. It seems that this
representation may therefore prove to be simpler than the phase
shift expansion usually used, and a more direct way to the scattering amplitudes.

7.10   Nucleon-Nucleon Scattering at Bev Energies

At energies of 1 Bev and above it is not fruitful to carry out a
phase shift analysis; there are too many states and all the phases
will become imaginary due to meson producing effects. A simpler
picture emerges of the optical model of the nucleon similar to that
of the nucleus (Chapter 10).

The forward angle pp nuclear scattering amplitude is almost
entirely imaginary. This may be seen by the complete lack of Cou-
lomb interference (Preston, 1960) whence we find $\mathrm{Re}\, A(0) \ll \mathrm{Im}\, A(0)$.
Moreover, the cross section is only a little greater than
the square of the imaginary part. From Preston (1960) we deduce
a discrepancy of 0.10 ± 0.05 b/sr out of a forward cross section of
0.55 b/sr. This discrepancy is confirmed by Azimov (1962), Bull
(1963), and Marquit (1962). This residue cannot be attributed

to a real scattering amplitude $A(0)$ so it must be attributed to the spin dependent scattering [B, E or F of equation (3-6)]. The polarization is small (Bareyre, 1961) confirming that Im A is the main term of the scattering amplitude.

The study of scattering cross section vs. the square of the momentum transfer q^2 then gives the size of this absorptive region. Just as in the nuclear case discussed in Chapter 10, the size should be correctly given by a simple impulse approximation type calculation although the magnitudes of the amplitudes are not.

The angular distribution has been measured and plotted from 6 to 25 Bev by Diddens (1962) and by Baker (1962). If the momentum distributions were the same, we would say that the absorptive region was of a constant size. In fact the absorptive region appears to increase in size with increasing energy, and at the same time to become more transparent to keep the total cross section roughly constant. The rms radius of the absorptive region at 3 Bev is found for example to be $(1.06 \pm 0.05) \times 10^{-13}$ cm, which is (1.29 ± 0.09) times the presently accepted rms radius of the proton charge or magnetic moment distribution found from electron scattering data. Since we have two interacting pion clouds for the proton-proton scattering, and only one for electron-proton scattering, a factor $= 1.41$ is reasonable.

Speculations about Regge poles suggest that the size of the absorptive region should so increase. They suggest that the cross section should be expressed in the form

$$\left(\frac{d\sigma}{dt}\right) = \left(\frac{d\sigma}{dt}\right)_{t=0} F(t) \left(\frac{S}{2M^2}\right)^{2(\alpha(t)-1)} \tag{7-13}$$

where $t = q^2$, S is the energy.

The form factor $F(t) = F(q^2)$ is now constant and the next term shows an energy dependence which is determined by the unknown function $\alpha(t)$. Figure 7-5 shows a plot of $\alpha(t)$ so derived from experiment. We note that at low values of momentum transfer and energy, the apparent size of the absorptive region stays constant and the simpler picture holds good. At high energies the increasing size

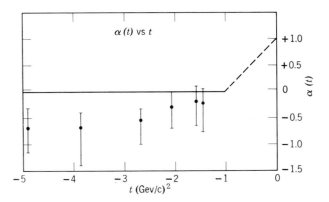

Figure 7-5. The t dependence of the Regge term $\alpha(t)$ of equation 7-13. The dotted line is a mean through many points (Baker 1962).

indicates that, relative to the core, the periphery of the proton interacts more strongly, although the overall interaction stays constant. The reason why all parts of the charge seem to interact equally strongly at 3 Bev, in order to agree with the size from electron scattering, is still obscure.

Chapter 8

Electromagnetic Studies of Nucleon-Nucleon Interactions

8.1 General

We have noted that elastic scattering of nucleons by nucleons can only tell us a limited amount of information. This can be seen when we notice that the centre of mass system before collision and the centre of mass system after collision must have the same momentum and energy. A formal way of stating this is that we only know the diagonal terms of the scattering matrix from nucleon-nucleon scattering; that we measure nucleon-nucleon scattering on the mass (or on the energy) shell.

An assumption is usually made that the elements of the scattering matrix vary slowly as we go off the mass shell. Of course if a nuclear potential is assumed, or dispersion theory, there is a specific recipe for discussing the results, or predictions, of experiments off the mass shell. We have tacitly assumed this in Chapter 2 where we compared data for the deuteron with low energy n-p scattering, and in the discussion of the nucleon-nucleon potentials in Chapter 7.

It is possible, in principle, to study off mass shell processes and thus verify our general assumptions by use of electromagnetic interactions, which are assumed to be completely understood. In Figure 8-1 we show the lowest order Feynman diagrams (a) for ordinary nucleon-nucleon scattering (b) for a simple radiative process, and (c) for a complex electromagnetic process involving electron scattering or pair production. The process (b) is called nucleon-nucleon bremsstrahlung. It is clear that the final two nucleon state has an energy different from the initial state by the gamma ray energy k_0 and the two cm systems differ in momentum by $\mathbf{k}$. But the energy and momentum changes may not separately be varied for we have $k_0{}^2 = \mathbf{k} \cdot \mathbf{k}$ for a real γ ray.

Nucleon-nucleon bremsstrahlung is a hard process to study (apart from the fact that there is a further infinity of possible experiments as compared to ordinary nucleon-nucleon scattering). The total cross section for emitting a photon of energy greater than $\frac{1}{2}$ the two nucleon cm energy is of the order of 10^{-29} to 10^{-30} cm^2 as compared to 10^{-25} to 10^{-26} cm^2 for the total elastic scattering

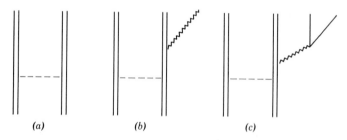

(a) (b) (c)

Figure 8-1. Diagrams illustrating (a) np scattering by one pion exchange, (b) np bremsstrahlung, and (c) np bremsstrahlung with internal pairs.

cross sections. This hard fact, and the absence of theoretical stimulation to select from among the extra infinity of variables, has limited experiments showing qualitatively that such a process exists. Some calculations have been made by Sobel (1963).

A specific case, however, is comparatively simple experimentally. When the two initial nucleons, instead of being free particles as in the process (Fig. 8-1b), are bound to form a deuteron. Here the angular distribution of the emitted particles has been studied, and now their polarization is being studied also. For zero energy gamma rays we have the inverse process of neutron-proton capture.

The extension to case (c) is even harder experimentally and involves another infinity—the variation with four momentum q transferred to the nucleon-nucleon system. It is even clearer that only in special cases will the experiments be possible. As the diagram is drawn we have an electron and positron in the final state. We can also specialize to the case of the initial neutron and proton forming a deuteron, and change the outgoing positron to an incoming electron. This case corresponds to elastic and inelastic electron scattering from the deuteron. At first sight these experiments sound much harder than the corresponding experiments on the photo-disintegration of the deuteron. This is indeed true if we wish to measure the angular distribution of the outgoing particles at a definite energy transfer to the system (energy of the virtual photon). But the situation is very different if we wish to measure the cross section integrated over all outgoing nucleons. This merely involves measuring the intensity of the electrons scattered from deuterons, at a given angle, as a function of the scattered electron energy. The techniques for this type of experiment have been sufficiently well developed that they may now be classed as "trivial" and therefore useful. We will not survey the techniques in detail in this book since they are well described elsewhere (Hofstadter, 1956, 1957).

Unfortunately, although the experiments on electron scattering from the deuteron (integrating over outgoing nucleons) and photo-disintegration of the deuteron, observing the outgoing nucleons, are well developed, the detailed theory of these is somewhat unrelated to the general development of the nucleon-nucleon interaction. When a fit to experiment has been obtained it is not clear to what extent particular features of the deuteron wavefunction are responsible for a fit or a lack of a fit. It is therefore not clear to what extent these experiments give new knowledge or merely confirm what is already known from the considerably more precise and more plentiful nucleon-nucleon scattering experiments.

In all the theoretical work so far, which always involves the deuteron in either the initial or final state or both, the assumption is made that the effect of the electromagnetic interactions is correctly taken into account by taking the interactions with the nucleons at the positions determined by the wavefunctions and that any more specific interactions of γ rays with meson currents exchanged between the nucleons (exchange currents) is absent. This assumption is based upon Siegert's theorem (Sachs, 1951, Brennan, 1952) which is proved for electric multipole interactions up to order v/c in the relative nucleon velocities (say 40 mev). The proof given which applies only to cases of zero momentum transfer, follows from the requirements of gauge invariance. Partial calculations of the deviations give varying results with varying sign. It may turn out that the effect of these exchange currents is the only effect which cannot be described by the on-the-energy-shell nucleon-nucleon scattering.

The theory also treats the deuteron nonrelativistically. The explicit parameterization of the effective range expansion in Chapter 2 also uses nonrelativistic wavefunctions, though the theory is basically relativistic. Hopefully, errors cancel when we compare the two.

8.2   Electron-Deuteron Elastic Scattering

The theory of electron interactions of nucleons and nuclei has been described elsewhere (Drell, 1961, Jankus, 1956, Durand, 1961). We use a theorem that the elastic and inelastic scattering of electrons can be expressed in terms of two invariant functions (form factors) of momentum transfer and energy transfer. It is convenient to express these in the helicity representation (Jacob, 1959). The form factors G_E and G_M enter the cross section formula as follows:

$$\frac{d\sigma}{d\Omega} = \left(\frac{e^2}{2E_0}\right)^2 \left\{\frac{1}{\sin^2\theta/2}\frac{1}{1+2E_0/M_c^2\sin^2\theta/2}\right\}$$

$$\times\left\{\frac{G_E^2(q^2,q_0)\cot^2\theta/2}{(1+q_0^2/q^2)} + \frac{q^2 G_M^2(q^2,q_0)}{4M^2c^2}\left[2+\frac{\cot^2\theta/2}{1+q_0^2/q^2}\right]\right\}$$

$$(8\text{-}1)$$

where for elastic scattering $q_0^2 = q^4/4M^2$ and the G_E and G_M become functions of one variable instead of two q^2 is the square of the invariant four momentum transfer and q_0 is the energy transfer.

The terms G_E and G_M correspond to scattering by the electric and magnetic fields, respectively, and can be easily separated by the angular dependence. G_E and G_M correspond to the effects of longitudinal and transverse virtual photons, and thus to no spin flip and spin flip of the interacting system. For inelastic scattering processes we find that at low q^2, G_M is given by the real photon cross section because G_E corresponds to zero helicity (longitudinal photons)

$$G_M(q^2, q_0) \rightarrow \sigma_\gamma(q_0) \qquad \text{as } q \rightarrow 0 \qquad (8\text{-}2)$$

Let us consider, for example, $G_E(q^2)$ for elastic scattering. Sachs (1962) shows that this is the Fourier transform of the charge distribution of the deuteron in its rest frame. We express this in terms of the properties of the deuteron by the relation which we state on intuitive grounds.

$$G_E(q^2) = 2G_{ES}(q^2)G_{Ed}(q^2) \qquad (8\text{-}3)$$

where $2G_{ES}(q^2)$ is the isotopic scalar sum of the neutron and proton charge form factors

$$2G_{ES}(q^2) = G_{En}(q^2) + G_{Ep}(q^2) \qquad (8\text{-}4)$$

and they describe the interaction of the γ ray with the nucleon in the diagram of Figure 7-1c. G_{Ed} should then be given by the neutron and proton wavefunctions in the deuteron rest frame (np cm system). The expectation is that this completely separates the electromagnetic interaction from the nuclear force problem. Siegert's theorem is here assumed to hold for the electric form factors. A knowledge of the nucleon form factors must be assumed before we may proceed further.

These arguments, based on equation 8-2, are not exact for the deuteron which has spin 1 and not $\frac{1}{2}$. The correct formula has been written by Gourdin (1962) and Jones (1962). The expression for G_E given above is verified though that for G_M becomes more complex.

We now follow Jankus' nonrelativistic theory for $G_{Ed}(q^2)$, though we hope we take account of the major relativistic effects by the relativistic separation just discussed. We must replace Jankus' 3 dimensional momentum transfer q in the electron deuteron cm system by a 3 dimensional transfer in the deuteron rest system. An additional kinematic factor $1 + q^2/4M^2$ is also needed relativistically (Jones, 1962).

Then we find

$$(1 + q^2/4M^2)\,|\,G_{Ed}(q^2)\,|^2 = \left|\,\int_0^\infty (\psi_g)^2 e^{i\mathbf{q}\cdot\mathbf{r}/2} d\mathbf{r}\,\right|^2 \qquad (8\text{-}5)$$

and by replacing ψ_g by ψ_s and ψ_D as in Chapter 2 we get

$$(1 + q^2/4M^2)\,|\,G_{Ed}(q^2)\,|^2 = N_g^{\,2}\left[\int_0^\infty (u^2 + w^2) j_0(qr/2) dr\right]^2$$

$$+ N_g^{\,2}\left[\int_0^\infty \left(uw - \frac{1}{\sqrt{8}}\,w^2\right)\right.$$

$$\left. \times j_2\left(\frac{qr}{2}\right) dr\right]^2$$

$$= N_g^{\,2}[G_{Ed}^c(q^2)]^2 + N_g^{\,2}[G_{Ed}^Q(q^2)]^2 \qquad (8\text{-}6)$$

where the independence of the two terms is ensured by the different angular dependence of the S and D states. We note that in the lowest order of the spherical harmonics j_0 and j_2, G_{Ed}^c gives unity [physically the charge e in equation (8-2)] and G_{Ed}^Q the quadrupole moment of the deuteron $(Q/50)$ as in equation (2-53). This, of course, is no accident.

Let us consider the "central" term $G_{Ed}^c(q^2)$. We may clearly add and subtract from it the asymptotic form of the deuteron ground state form factors found in equation (2-3).

$$G_{Ed}^c(q^2) = N_g^{\,2}\int_0^\infty e^{-2\gamma r} j_0\left(\frac{qr}{2}\right) dr$$

$$+ N_g^{\,2}\int_0^\infty (u^2 + w^2 - e^{-2\gamma r}) j_0\left(\frac{qr}{2}\right) dr \qquad (8\text{-}7)$$

We have separated the contributions to $G_{ED}^c(q^2)$ into two parts; that dependent on the parts of the deuteron wavefunction *outside* the range of forces, and that inside. We note that the former part is determined principally by γ, which is known to 0.05% from the deuteron binding energy (Chapter 2) and partially by $\rho(-\epsilon, -\epsilon)$, which is also known. The second term in (8-7) can then be expanded. In most cases it is small because the quadrupole moment is small, and can be treated as a correction.

We now evaluate explicitly the first term of (8-7) and expand the second. Using the known normalization $\int (u^2 + w^2)dr = 1$ we get

$$G_{Ed}^c(q^2) = \frac{2}{q} N_g^2 \tan^{-1}\left(\frac{q}{4\gamma}\right) - N_g^2$$

$$+ N_g^2 \frac{q^2}{24} \int_0^\infty r^2[(u^2 + w^2) - e^{-2\gamma r}]$$

$$+ \frac{q^4 N_g^2}{1920} \int_0^\infty r^4[u^2 + w^2 - e^{-2\gamma r}]dr + \text{etc.} \quad (8\text{-}8)$$

We thus notice that the new nuclear information is contained in the coefficients of q^{2n} in (8-8). We rewrite the effective range definition and define

$$\rho(-\epsilon, -\epsilon) \equiv -2\int [(u^2 + w^2) - e^{2\gamma r}]dr \qquad (8\text{-}9)$$

$$\rho'(-\epsilon, -\epsilon) \equiv -2\int r^2[(u^2 + w^2) - e^{-2\gamma r}]dr \qquad (8\text{-}10)$$

$$\rho''(-\epsilon, -\epsilon) \equiv -2\int r^4[(u^2 + w^2) - e^{-2\gamma r}]dr \qquad (8\text{-}11)$$

The experiments (MacIntyre, 1957, 1958, Friedman, 1960) have been carried to momentum transfers $q = 3 \times 10^{13}$ cm^{-1}.

The experiments have been compared with numerical calculations based on three wavefunctions—the Gartenhaus, and two

Yukawa functions of Feshbach and Schwinger. These differ in that the first has a 7% D state and a repulsive core, and the 2nd and 3rd have 2 and 4% D states. It becomes clear that the main difference in the effect of these functions is the parameter ρ' defined in (8-10).

If we reasonably restrict $u^2 + w^2$ never to proceed above the asymptotic value of $e^{-2\gamma r}$, the smallest possible parameter ρ' consistent with a given ρ is given by a wavefunction which rises suddenly from zero to its asymptotic value at a value r given by

$$\gamma\rho = 1 - e^{-2\gamma r} \qquad (8\text{-}12)$$

whence

$$r = 1.1 \times 10^{-13} \text{ cm}$$

and

$$\rho' = 0.65 \times 10^{-39} \text{ cm}^2$$

$$\rho'' = 0.45 \times 10^{-65} \text{ cm}^2$$

The contributions to $G_{Ed}^c(q^2)$ at $q = 3$ fermi becomes $+0.08$ from ρ' and -0.013 from ρ''. In this extreme case only ρ' contributes.

We also note that ρ', ρ'' are larger for the Hulthén potential and intermediate for square well. Fortunately the conclusions about the value of the parameter ρ' do not depend critically on G_{ES}. This is because at $q = 2.94 \times 10^{13}$ cm^{-1} the first two terms of (8-8) cancel leaving only the correction terms. Thus the error on ρ' is proportional to the error in G_{ES} and not magnified by a difference effect.

At the present moment the calculations of the nuclear properties represented by ρ' and ρ'' is probably more precise than the values of G_{ES} (Glendenning, 1962). Therefore the fashionable procedure is to derive G_{ES} from this experiment. Figure 8-2 shows G_{ES} so derived by Glendenning.

A recent measurement by Drickey (1962), with a precision increased by a factor of 5, suggests when analyzed by these procedures that $G_{En} = 0$ at all q^2, in disagreement with the low energy neutron-electron interaction. This is, no doubt, a breakdown in theory, probably in equation 8-3.

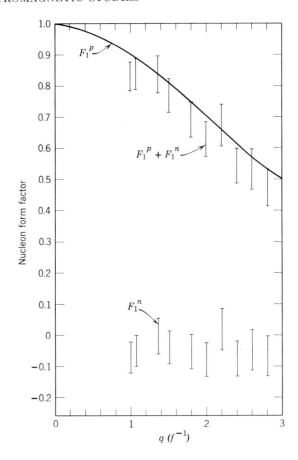

Figure 8-2. Neutron form factor and isotopic scalar nucleon form factor derived by Glendenning *et al.* from elastic *ed* scattering using calculations equivalent to those here.

If G_{ES} is measured precisely in other ways, and almost certainly at higher values of q^2, the argument will be reversed and we will revert to the procedure of the original authors of deriving information about the deuteron.

This experiment has been claimed by the original authors as direct evidence for a repulsive core. Evidence it surely is, but the data is sensitive only to the asymptotic part of the wavefunction and that given by one pion exchange as equations (8-5) to (8-11) show. The sensitivity to the core is entirely in the normalization N_g. A wavefunction which has the asymptotic shape and fits one pion exchange can only give the experimental value for the normalization if it has a repulsive core.

Similar considerations apply to the magnetic moment term G_M in (8-2), but now we can only separate the deuteron part by putting:

$$G_M(q^2) = \tfrac{2}{3} 2 G_{Md}(q^2) G_{MS}(q^2) \qquad (8\text{-}12)$$

The part of this which depends upon the deuteron is similar to that in (8-5) to (8-8) so this equation has been used (Friedman, 1960) to determine $G_{MS}(q^2)$ and verify that $G_{MS} = (G_{Mp} + G_{Mn})$ is small compared with $G_{MV} = (G_{Mp} - G_{Mn})$. The factor $\tfrac{2}{3}$ is the statistical probability of a spin flip transition without breaking up the deuteron. Jones (1962) has shown that the magnetic deuteron form factor G_{Md} is not quite so simple as the electric form factor (8-6).

If we place $q^2 = 0$ in Jones' formula for the magnetic form factor, we obtain equation 2-64, which has the complication of the term p_D. Even this is in error by a few percent as discussed in Chapter 2.

8.3   Inelastic Scattering from the Deuteron

We can extend the considerations of the elastic scattering to the slightly inelastic scattering. There are two types of transitions; leaving the final system in either the ^1S final state or the ^3S final state. The former contributes only to G_M and the latter to G_E. Let us consider the former. It is a spin flip transition, and at $q \to 0$ it becomes the same process as discussed already in Chapter 2—the disintegration of the deuteron at low energies, and the inverse of the neutron capture process. This proceeds by the integral [see Chapter 2, equation (2-46)]

$$\int u_g(\mu_p - \mu_n) u_S \, dr \qquad (8\text{-}13)$$

The factor $\mu_p - \mu_n$ is the isotopic vector magnetic moment of the nucleons. The extension of this to higher momentum transfers is obvious

$$2G_{MV} \int u_g u_S e^{i\mathbf{q} \cdot \mathbf{r}/2} dr \qquad (8\text{-}14)$$

In this calculation G_{MV} can be directly taken, and exchange moments are usually neglected. Yet we know that at $q = 0$ there is a $6 \pm 2\%$ term [equation (2-49)] from exchange currents and this is likely to be larger at large q.

For the transition to the ^3S state the appropriate matrix element becomes

$$2G_{ES} \int u_g z u_S dr \qquad (8\text{-}15)$$

These formulae have been derived direct from the Hamiltonian by Jankus (1956) and Durand (1961) using a different and more complicated set of form factors.

In experiments on the slightly inelastic scattering (Kendall, 1961, Peterson, 1961) what is measured for the ^3S to ^1S transition is a ratio to proton scattering $(G_M^2 G_{MV}^2)/F_p^2$ although they quote G_M^2. The values they took for the ratio G_{MV}/F_p are early ones, but correspond quite closely to that now accepted. Thus, to within the error on G_{MV}^2 of about 10%, they have correctly measured G_M^2. For the $^3S \rightarrow {}^3S$ transition they measure $G_E^2 G_{ES}^2/F_p^2$. G_{ES} is uncertain due to the electron neutron interactions, and they took it equal to zero, and $F_p \simeq G_{Ep}$. This also is quite close to presently accepted values. The two transitions were not completely separated at the angles they used.

With the considerable uncertainties, they compared their experiments with theory assuming that the radial wavefunctions u_g and u_S come firstly from a potential *without* a repulsive core; secondly a repulsive core is included in u_g only; and thirdly a repulsive core is included in both u_g and u_S. No exchange moment was included. This comparison is shown in Figure 8-3. It is gratifying that the assumption of a repulsive core gives the best fit, as it did with the elastic scattering. Inclusion of an exchange term would increase the evidence for a repulsive core. Again care must be exercised in talk-

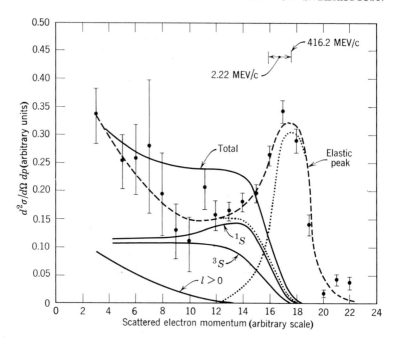

Figure 8-3. Momentum distribution of electrons scattered from the deuteron showing the slightly inelastic events. The lines are the calculations using a wavefunction without a repulsive core in the various states. The low cross section is attributed to the effect of the core (Kendall).

ing about the core. The sensitivity to the core is only through the wavefunction normalization, and the data is sensitive solely to the asymptotic part of the wavefunction and that part that depends on one pion exchange.

8.4   Photodisintegration of the Deuteron

A particular case of inelastic scattering from the deuteron, a limit of G_M as $q \rightarrow 0$, is the photodisintegration. Although theoretically it is a special case, experimentally entirely different parameters are studied. In experiments on electron scattering the scattered electron alone is observed, and an integration is made over all other particles. In photodisintegration experiments the angular distribution and polarization of the outgoing particles is studied. The electrodisintegration experiments correspond in total cross section measurements at a certain q.

By studying the angular distribution of the outgoing particles one hopes to separate the contributions of different angular momentum states.

Experiments have used two methods; firstly, photographic plates to detect the protons, and secondly a counter telescope. There has been very poor agreement between them. The energy of the protons must be measured to define the γ-ray energy responsible for the disintegration, for there is a continuous spectrum of γ rays. If there is any bias in this energy measurement, the angular distribution will be incorrect.

The monitoring of the γ-ray intensity is also hard. Variations of 10 to 20% between laboratories has been common. Some of the data are shown in Figures 8-4 and 8-5. It is clear that a definitive measurement is needed, though the results of Galey (1960) look promising. Probably a magnetic spectrometer will be needed.

The measurements of the photodisintegration of the deuteron were, until recently, analysed in terms of the following angular distribution:

$$\frac{d\sigma}{d\Omega} = A(\sin^2\theta)(1 - \beta\cos\theta) + B \qquad (8\text{-}16)$$

The term in A corresponds mainly to ^3S to ^3P transitions of the nucleons, the β term given by dipole/quadrupole interference ($^3S \rightarrow {}^3P$ and $^3S \rightarrow {}^3D$ transitions) and B is the contribution from $^3S \rightarrow {}^1S$ transitions. The calculations neglected the deuteron D state, binding in the final states, and used a Hulthén potential.

Experiment failed to agree with the predictions (Bishop, 1957, Hulthén, 1957). In particular, although the total cross section was not unreasonable, the coefficient A was experimentally smaller than expected, and B was too large.

If a potential with a repulsive core were used, the prediction for A would have been greater; little effect was found by adding in

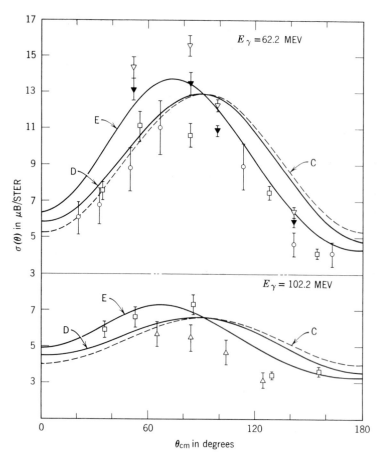

Figure 8-4. Differential cross section for the $d(\gamma, n)p$ reaction for 62.2 and 102.2 mev. Data are: ○, Allen (1955), 66 mev; □, Whalin (1956), 65 and 105 mev; △, Keck (1956), 105 mev; ▽, Galey (1960), 60 and 65 mev. The theoretical lines are those of Zickendraht.

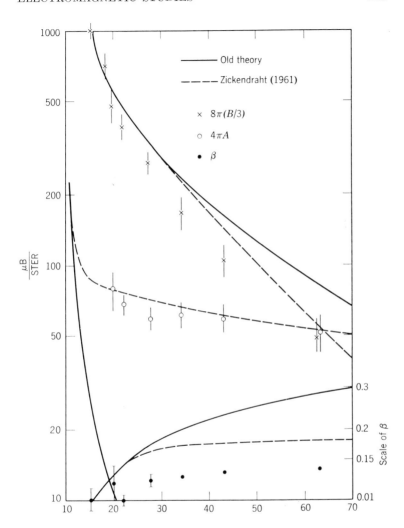

Figure 8-5. Parameters A, B, β in equation 8-17 versus energy. The data are those of Allen. The solid lines are old calculations; the dotted ones, new calculations of Zickendraht. The data of Galey would increase β.

effects from the binding in the ^3P state, with experimental phases given from pp scattering.

It seems that two important items are necessary for a complete theoretical picture. Firstly the D state of the deuteron must be assumed to have a large probability (7%) compared to that (2–3%) assumed before, and secondly the correct coupling of all the states $^3P_2$–$^3F_2$, etc., must be included. This has all been calculated by assuming a phenomenological potential, which fits the scattering data. The work by deSwart (1959), Rustgi (1960), Zickendraht (1961) and Donnachie (1962) is the most extensive. The large D state probability increases the term B and reduces A by the transitions $^3D \rightarrow {}^3P$. Agreement is found with ^3P phases as given in Chapter 7. Alternate phase shift solutions which give a different ordering of these phases are not acceptable, though the exact values may not be important.

We present in Figure 8-4 a comparison of some experimental data. The approximations C, D and E correspond to progressively adding in extra terms. In approximation D already included are $E_1(^3S_1 + {}^3D_1) \rightarrow {}^3P_0, {}^3P_1, ({}^3P_2 + {}^3F_2)$; $M_1(^3S_1 + {}^3D_1) \rightarrow {}^1S_0$, $^1D_2$; $M_1(^3S_1 + {}^3D_1) \rightarrow ({}^3S_1 + {}^3D_1)^3D_2$; and in the approximation E the E_2 transitions $^3S_2 + {}^3D_1 \rightarrow ({}^3D_1 + {}^3S_1), {}^3D_2, ({}^3D_3 + {}^3G_3)$ are included. The comparison shows fair agreement. The agreement looks better on a log plot of the data as a function of energy (Figure 8-5), where the "elementary" and the correct theoretical predictions are compared. To avoid confusion of the plot of Figure 8-5, only the data of Allen is used.

The fair agreement suggests that Siegert's theorem is probably valid for the processes under study up to 70 mev and that the potential used gives an adequate description of the ground state of the deuteron and the final states used.

The polarization of the outgoing protons and neutrons from photodisintegration has recently been measured by many authors (Bertozzi, 1963, White, 1963, Gorenstein, 1963, Frederic, 1963). The results of the first two experiments are in general agreement with the theory discussed above. The other two are at a sufficiently high energy (300 mev) that mesonic effects are all important.

Chapter 9

Conservation Laws

The discussion of the previous chapters has mostly assumed that parity, and even isotopic spin, are conserved and time reversal is valid. It is possible in principle to perform all the experiments in Table 3-1 and by comparison to verify that there is no violation of these conservation laws. In practice this is too large an undertaking and selected experiments only are performed.

9.1 Time Reversal

Experiments on time reversal all involve a comparison of the experiments on either side of the principal diagonal in Table 3-1; in particular a comparison between the asymmetry in pp scattering of a polarized beam, and the polarization by scattering of an unpolarized beam. The comparison of the beam polarization and the power of the analyzing scattering thus depends upon the formula (3-5) for the polarizer and analyzer. Thus time reversal invariance must be assumed for proton scattering from carbon at one angle. It may then be verified for scattering at other angles, and with other targets. Polarization and asymmetry have been compared for hydrogen at one angle and energy each by Hillmann (1958) (at 180 mev and 30.9° cm) and Abashian (1958) (at 210 mev and 30° cm) to a precision of 0.02 each (i.e., $P - A = 0.029 \pm 0.018$ at 210 mev. At 142 mev at each of eight angles from 12° to 82° cm $P - A$ has been measured to 0.02 (Hwang, 1960, Bird, 1961). See Figure 9-1. It has been consistently assumed therefore that time reversal is always valid.

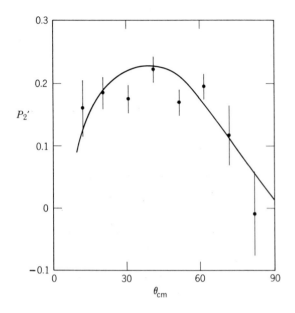

Figure 9-1. A comparison of P_2', the polarization measured in pp scattering at 142 mev, with the asymmetry measurements (solid line) (Hwang).

9.2 Parity

Parity nonconservation has been studied by looking for polarization in the scattering plane after a single scattering of an unpolarized beam. One of the most accurate high-energy measurements is that of Jones (1958), at Liverpool. Protons of 380 mev bombarded a beryllium target in the cyclotron and neutrons were produced in the forward direction, corresponding except for binding, to 180° np scattering. A search was made for longitudinal polarization of the beam. This was done by causing the neutron spin to precess in the cyclotron magnet and another magnet till it was transverse to the motion; an up/down np scattering then was used to analyze for polarization. The spin precession magnet was reversed and adjusted to reverse the spin direction, but there was no change in counting rate. From this experiment an upper limit of 0.004 is set for the ratio of parity nonconserving to parity conserving scattering amplitude at this angle and energy. This ratio is often called F.

Experiments on nucleon-nucleon scattering often include a search for parity nonconservation as a by-product, usually as a check on the apparatus. Thus an up/down asymmetry in a double scattering experiment in which the first scattering is, as usual, in a horizontal plane, gives such a check. This has been done for pp scattering to an accuracy of about 0.02 at several angles and energies (for references see Table 5-3). A more specific search has been made for the parity nonconserving parameters P_{in}, P_{ie}, P_2' in equation (3-9) as a by-product of a triple scattering experiment to measure R in pp scattering (Thorndike, 1961).

More precise limits on parity conserving interactions may be set by low-energy nuclear physics. Certain transitions between energy levels are forbidden if parity is conserved, and a search for such transitions tests parity conservation (Boehm, 1959, Wilkinson, 1961, Grodzins, 1961). In the absence of such effects it is still possible to have a momentum dependent interaction that would only appear at high energies, so the less precise high-energy data is still important.

None of these tests show any deviation from parity conservation. A deviation is to be expected, however, according to the conserved vector current theory of weak interactions. According to this theory the interactions Hamiltonian for weak interactions is

$$H_{\text{int}} = \tfrac{1}{2}[j_\mu \tilde{\gamma}_\mu + \text{Hermitian conjugate}] \qquad (9\text{-}1)$$

and

$$j_\mu = G^{\frac{1}{2}}\{i\overline{N} + \gamma_\mu(1 + \gamma_5)N + i\bar{\nu}\gamma_\mu(1 + \gamma_5)e$$
$$- i\sqrt{2}\,[\pi + \partial_\mu\pi_0 - \pi_0\partial_\mu\pi_+] + \cdots \qquad (9\text{-}2)$$

where N, ν, e, π are field functions for the nucleon neutrino and electron and a π meson. $G \simeq 10^{-49}$ erg cm^3.

The ordinary neutrino decay comes from a cross term between the first two terms. A parity nonconserving internucleon interaction can arise from the square of the first term, or the cross term between the first and third. The latter is likely to be strongest and it has been estimated by Blin-Stoyle (1960) who calculates that the ratio of parity nonconserving to parity conserving interaction is of the order

$$F = G/\mu_c r = 10^{-7} \qquad (9\text{-}3)$$

where r is the radius of the interaction. This is just below the limit of detectability.

9.3   Charge Independence

Evidence for charge independence came from the equality of effective interaction potentials for singlet np and pp scattering. The scattering lengths are not equal; both are large and negative, corresponding to singlet states unbound. The inequality corresponds to a difference in well depth of $1\frac{1}{2}\%$ if a square potential well is assumed. It is not possible to subtract the effects of the Coulomb interaction within the range of nuclear forces in a model independent way. For example, Schwinger (1950) showed that for a strong interaction at small distances given by a Yukawa potential the magnetic moment interaction can account for the $1\frac{1}{2}\%$. This is no longer the case, however, if a repulsive core is used or if the finite extension of the magnetic structure of the nucleons is considered (Salpeter, 1951, Riazuddin, 1958).

Wong (1962) calculates the effect of the $\pi^- \pi^0$ mass difference using a partial wave dispersion relation and finds a difference of the right magnitude.

The assumption of charge independence is used also to complete the neutron-proton phase shift analysis of Chapter 7. The pion-nucleon coupling constant in the OPEP term was separately varied for the np and pp interactions and good agreement was achieved (Breit, 1960, 1962). The boundary condition model also required equality for two pion terms (TPEP) (Breit, 1961, Feshbach, 1961). Thus the long range part of the potential is charge independent. A charge dependent term may turn up in the core. Such suggestions were made by Fubini (1961) and Glashow (1961). The only satisfactory way of disentangling such an interaction would seem to be an analysis such as that of Feshbach (1961) with charge dependent constants at the boundary. At the moment data is probably inadequate for such a search.

The less stringent conditions of charge symmetry have also been studied. At low energies, the aim is to find the nn scattering length. All attempts to find a bound dineutron have failed, showing that this scattering length is negative. A strong interaction is found, however, in any interaction involving two neutrons in a final ^1S state. A study of one of these may be used as a measure of the nn interaction.

One such measure is the spectrum of γ rays from the capture of π^- mesons by the deuteron (Phillips, 1954)

$$\pi^- + D \rightarrow N + N + \gamma \tag{9-4}$$

In the absence of a neutron-neutron interaction statistical phase space arguments give the distribution of γ ray energies. However, the nn attraction forces the two neutrons to come out in a low-energy S state. The width of the γ ray spectrum gives a measure of scattering length. The instrumental resolution is determined by measuring the monochromatic γ ray from the capture of slow π^- mesons by protons. The result is

$$a_{nn} = -15.9 \times 10^{-13} \text{ cm} \tag{9-5}$$

with error limits of -8.5 to $-\infty$.

Another measurement, which involves more detailed theoretical understanding, comes from a measure of the spectrum of high-energy protons in the scattering of 20 mev neutrons by deuterons

$$n + d \rightarrow n + n + P \tag{9-6}$$

Again the neutrons come out in a low-energy S state. Such a measurement and accompanying calculation, has been reported (Ilakovac, 1961).

A few high-energy nn cross section measurements have been performed by inelastic nd scattering (Dzelepov, 1954). A beam of 350 or 600 mev neutrons was allowed to fall in turn on deuterons and on protons. Neutrons scattered from the deuterons or protons were measured and found to have intensities I_D and I_p, respectively. The nn cross section was derived from the formula

$$\sigma_{nn} = \sigma_{np}(I_d - I_p)/I_p \qquad (9\text{-}7)$$

The results are accurate to $\pm 20\%$ and are consistent with the charge symmetry assumption $\sigma_{nn} = \sigma_{pp}$.

Other, more precise tests come from the total neutron-deuteron scattering cross section. If charge independence is valid we expect

$$\sigma_{nd}(\text{total}) = \sigma_{pp}(\text{total}) + \sigma_{np}(\text{total}) \qquad (9\text{-}8)$$

when due allowance is made for Coulomb effects. This is indeed achieved to an accuracy of about 5% (see Appendix). This agreement includes possible errors in the accuracy of the impulse approximation used in setting up equation (9-8). Such errors are of course present in the other tests.

Probably the best evidence for the equality of the pp and nn forces (charge symmetry) still comes from the multiplet levels in light nuclei. This is outside the scope of this book.

Chapter 10

The Scattering of Nucleons from Light Nuclei

10.1 Impulse Approximation for Elastic Scattering

One aspect of the scattering of nucleons from light nuclei has already been considered in Chapter 3 where the inelastic scattering from the deuteron was related to the nucleon-nucleon scattering, and used in Chapter 6 to give direct information about the neutron proton system. This chapter will further develop the theory for elastic scattering.

There are three reasons why the scattering from light nuclei is relevant to the purpose of this book. Firstly, there may be information about the interaction between two nucleons contained therein which is not easily obtained by direct nucleon-nucleon scattering. Inelastic proton-deuteron scattering has already been discussed in Chapter 3. Secondly, the extent to which two body interactions can account for all the phenomena involved is an indication of the role 3 body forces must play in the structure of nuclei. Thirdly, the scattering of nucleons by nucleons does not uniquely determine the 2 body nucleon-nucleon interaction but only the matrix elements on the mass (energy) shell. The use of radiative processes to provide other information is discussed in Chapter 8. Scattering from light nuclei might provide some also. Unfortunately it will be found that the available calculational techniques fail just in those regions where information about our second and third aims might possibly be extracted.

153

The impulse approximation used in Chapter 3 was in fact devised by Chew (1952) just for the problem of elastic scattering. As in the application of Chapter 3 the wavelength of the incident particle must be smaller than the nucleus and smaller than the distance between nucleons in the nucleus. This holds for incident nucleons of 150 mev lab. Again the approximation consists of assuming that the incident nucleon interacts with only one nucleon at a time in the nucleus, and that during the short time duration of this interaction the struck nucleon may be considered to be free. Clearly the following condition must hold:

$$\lambda \ll R \qquad (10\text{-}1)$$

where R is the radius of the nucleus. In addition for this problem the approximation is made of assuming that all struck nucleons are stationary and all multiple scattering is neglected. This approximation is formally equivalent to that discussed in Chapter 2 to obtain the np coherent amplitude f from neutron scattering by ortho and parahydrogen. There, however, the range of the interaction was orders of magnitude smaller than the molecular dimensions. Here the approximation is only marginally valid.

The nucleus contains several discrete nucleons and in the example shown, an equal number of protons and neutrons with an equal density distribution $\rho(r)$. The incident neutron has a small wavelength and a definite trajectory. The nucleus spin is assumed zero. In the forward direction the nucleon-nucleon scattering *amplitudes* add directly to give a scattering amplitude.

$$G(0) + \sigma \cdot \mathbf{n} H(0) = Z A_{np}(0) + (A - Z) A_{nn}(0)$$
$$+ \sigma \cdot \mathbf{n} [Z C_{np}(0) + (A - Z) C_{nn}(0)] \quad (10\text{-}2)$$

where the coefficients A, C are coefficients of the nucleon-nucleon scattering matrix (3-6). The coefficients BEF in the nucleon-nucleon scattering amplitudes do not contribute, because they correspond to a flip of the spin of the struck particle. Each of these terms in equation (3-6) contains the parameter σ_2 which may not be included (Tamor, 1955). Inclusion of σ_2 is not consistent with the maintenance of spin zero of the struck nucleus. They contribute instead to inelastic scattering processes.

At an angle θ, there will be interference between the amplitudes of scattering from different parts of the nucleus as shown. It can be seen at once that the interference between a central ray and a ray at a distance r from the center is

$$\exp\left[i(\mathbf{k} - \mathbf{k}') \cdot \mathbf{r}\right] = \exp\left(i\mathbf{q} \cdot \mathbf{r}\right) \qquad (10\text{-}3)$$

where $\mathbf{q} = \mathbf{k} - \mathbf{k}'(\simeq 2k \sin \frac{1}{2}\theta \simeq k\theta]$ is the momentum transfer. The scattering amplitude then becomes

$$G(q) + \boldsymbol{\sigma} \cdot \mathbf{n} H(q) = \{ZA_{np}(q) + (A - Z)A_{nn}(q)$$
$$+ \boldsymbol{\sigma} \cdot \mathbf{n}[ZC_{np}(q) + (A - Z)C_{nn}(q)]\}F(q) \qquad (10\text{-}4)$$

where $F(q) = \dfrac{1}{A} \displaystyle\int \rho(r)e^{i\mathbf{q} \cdot \mathbf{r}} d\mathbf{r}$ is the familiar form factor of the nucleus. $\rho(r)$ is the density distribution of nucleons and is assumed to be the same for protons and neutrons.

This formula is expressed in nonrelativistic terms; provided relativistic kinematics are used for $\mathbf{k}$, $\mathbf{k}'$, and $\mathbf{q}$ it remains valid, for we are rarely concerned with large q. In this formula the nucleon-nucleon amplitudes are expressed in the *laboratory* system of the struck nucleon. This choice is convenient, for it avoids carrying through kinematic factors.

With these equations for G and H it is possible to write at once the formulae for the experimental quantities, cross section, polarization, depolarization, rotation, etc.

$$\sigma(q) = G^2 + H^2$$
$$\sigma(q)P(q) = 2 \operatorname{Re} G^*H$$
$$= 2(\operatorname{Re} G \operatorname{Re} H + \operatorname{Im} G \operatorname{Im} H)$$
$$D(q) = 1$$
$$\sigma(R \cos \theta + A \sin \theta) = G^2 - H^2$$
$$\sigma(R \sin \theta - A \cos \theta) = 2 \operatorname{Im} G^*H \qquad (10\text{-}5)$$

A comparison of equation (10-5) with Table 3-2 shows that $P(q)$ is, in general, different for scattering from a nucleus than from a nucleon. Also, since the "spin flip" terms E and F in the nucleon-nucleon scattering matrix appear in the cross section and therefore the denominator only of the expression for $P(\theta)$, their exclusion increases P. This was first found experimentally, and it is amusing to recall, the fact was widely disbelieved because it appeared impossible to understand theoretically. The fact is of importance for all measurements of polarization for it is possible, as discussed in Chapter 4 to choose a polarizer or analyzer with a large cross section and high analyzing power. We also note that in the formulae for R and A, $\cos\theta$ and $\sin\theta$ enter whereas $\cos\theta/2$ and $\sin\theta/2$ enter in Table 3-2. The difference is due to our use here of the laboratory coordinate system.

As they stand, these equations omit the effects of multiple nuclear scattering. On physical grounds, multiple scattering is expected to remove particles approximately from the forward direction and scatter them into large angles. Calculations confirm the relative angular distribution is little affected for $qR < 2$, where R is the radius of the nucleus. The cross section is depressed, and the polarization and rotation parameters are almost the same as those without multiple scattering.

For proton scattering the same formulae apply, but the Coulomb scattering must be included. At high energies and for light nuclei, Bethe (1958) has shown that this may be done by adding a term (primarily real) to $G(q)$ directly proportional to $\dfrac{1}{\theta^2} F(q)$ due to the interaction of the charges, and a small term to $H(q)$, also proportional to $\dfrac{1}{\theta^2} F(q)$ due to the interaction of the proton's magnetic moment with the Coulomb field. These approximations enable the amplitudes G and H to be easily derived from experiment.

For a nucleus with spin, some remnant of the spin flip parameters BEF remain. Now the target nucleon may have its spin changed *without* altering the total spin of the target nucleon—merely its direction. Thus for neutron-deuteron scattering we find the parameters B, E, and F enter with factors $2/3$. For other nuclei the spins of the individual nucleons mostly cancel giving much smaller factors.

For more exact computations of the multiple scattering it is convenient to define a nuclear potential. We here take it to be of the general form

$$V(r) = V_R(r) + iV_I(r) + k^2 \boldsymbol{\sigma} \cdot \mathbf{L} \frac{d}{dr} [V_{RS}(r) + iV_{IS}(r)] \quad (10\text{-}6)$$

The values are defined to be those to give the correct scattering amplitude when used in Born approximation; $\mathbf{L}$ is the angular momentum vector $\mathbf{k} \times \mathbf{r}$. Thus

$$\int V(r) e^{i\mathbf{q} \cdot \mathbf{r}} d\mathbf{r} = G(q) + \boldsymbol{\sigma} \cdot \mathbf{n} H(q) \quad (10\text{-}7)$$

If the nucleon-nucleon amplitudes are taken to be constant with angle, the equation yields at once

$$\rho(0) V(r) = \rho(r)[V_R(0) + iV_I(0)]$$
$$+ k^2 \boldsymbol{\sigma} \cdot \mathbf{L}[V_{RS}(0) + iV_{IS}(0)] \frac{ld}{rdr} (\rho(r)) \quad (10\text{-}8)$$

This corresponds to a neglect of the range of nuclear forces. Then, for example,

$$\int_0^\infty V_R(r) dr = \text{Re} [Z A_{np}(0) + (A - Z) A_{nn}(0)] \quad (10\text{-}9)$$

The meanings of the potential $V(r)$ can be seen by expanding the quantities F, A, C in q^2 to give

$$F(q^2) = 1 - (r^2 q^2 / 6)$$

$$\text{Re } A(q^2) = 1 - (a^2_R q^2 / 6)$$

$$\text{Im } A(q^2) = 1 - (a^2_I q^2 / 6) \quad (10\text{-}10)$$

where r^2 is the mean square radius of the nucleus. The scattering cross section can also be expanded to give, in this approximation,

$$\sigma(\theta) = \sigma(0)[1 - R^2 q^2/6] \qquad (10\text{-}11)$$

where

$$R^2 = r^2 + a^2$$

The radius of the nucleus, R, determined from small angle elastic nucleon-nucleon scattering is thus larger than the true radius r. The quantity a has, in general, different real and imaginary parts and different magnitudes also for the spin orbit potential. This increase is due to the range of nuclear forces; for if nuclear forces had zero range, A and C would be constant and a would be zero.

In deriving the value of $F(q)$ from electron scattering experiments, the best method available, it must be remembered that the charge distribution is measured. It is usual, and probably correct, to assume that protons and neutrons have the same density distribution. Protons have an extended charge and thus the electron scattering experiments (Hofstadter, 1956, 1957) measure

$$F_{e\text{Nucl}}(q) = F_{ep}(q)F(q) \qquad (10\text{-}12)$$

where $F_{ep}(q)$ is the form factor for electron proton scattering. This equation is, of course, similar in form to equation 10-4.

Equation 10-12 is not quite exact; it is subject to small corrections just as equation 8-3 for the deuteron was subject to corrections.

The full potential of equation (10-8) has been used in a WKB approximation by (Cromer, 1959) to evaluate the multiple scattering. The procedure is only justifiable for small angles ($qR < 2$). At the present time it seems impossible to define rigorously a potential valid for all angles. Such attempts have had to assume the range of nuclear forces small compared with the size of the nucleus. This can lead to errors of 30%.

The formalism for including other effects is included in the paper of Kerman (1959), following Riesenfeld (1956) and Bethe (1958). It should also be noted that the comparison of nucleon-nucleus amplitudes and nucleon-nucleon amplitudes implied in equation (10-2) is not exact for large q because the energy conservation is not the same for the bound collisions as for the free collisions. If a nucleon-nucleon scattering *potential* is assumed, this may be calculated (Herzenberg, 1960). No calculations have yet been made with a potential carefully adjusted to fit the small angle nucleon-nucleon scattering data.

An interesting recent approach is to calculate the potential direct from the OPEP term in nucleon-nucleon scattering, neglecting all others. Quite a good fit is achieved (Moravcsik, 1961), which is probably accidental.

10.2   Elastic Scattering: Comparison with Experiment

Table 10-1 shows the wealth of experiments so far performed on this subject, at energies over 80 mev. Table 10-2 shows companion experiments on total and absorption cross sections. The discussion below is confined to the experiments in two regions; those at 310–350 mev and those at 135–146 mev. For these energies data is fairly complete for scattering from carbon.

Figure 10-1 shows a comparison of the PC and NC data at 310–350 mev. The point for neutron-carbon scattering at $q = 0$ is a minimum value given by the optical theorem given also in (3-1)

$$\sigma(0) > k^2 \sigma_{tot}^2 / 16\pi^2 \qquad (10\text{-}13)$$

The neutron data clearly extrapolate to this value. There is also little Coulomb interference with the predominantly real Coulomb scattering. These independently suggest Re $G(0)$ is small.

By contrast Figure 10-2 shows that at 135 mev there is a large Coulomb interference and $\sigma(0)$ is double the minimum value. In fact the difference is so large that difficulty has been found in fitting both proton-carbon and neutron-carbon scattering data simultaneously (Wilson, 1959).

This difficulty remains at 95 mev (Salmon, 1960), and it seems as if *all* neutron scattering data give cross sections systematically high by 20% or the proton data cross sections low by 20%. The radius from the neutron data also comes out a little large. These effects are discussed further in 10-4.

Figure 10-3 shows the normalized cross sections for neutron-carbon scattering vs. q. It is clear that the form factor $F^2(q)$ does not describe the data, and the angular dependence of A and C must be included; this angular dependence is different at 135 and 310 mev. The same conclusions can be reached from proton-helium and proton-deuteron scattering (Figures 10-4 and 10-5).

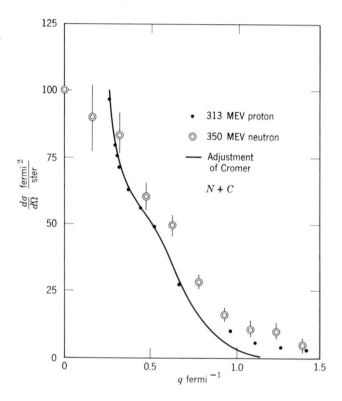

Figure 10-1. Cross section for $P + C$ (313 mev) and $N + C$ (350 mev) scattering versus momentum transfer q fermi^{-1}. The solid line is the adjustment of Cromer (1959).

TABLE 10-1   ELASTIC SCATTERING EXPERIMENTS OF
NUCLEONS ON LIGHT NUCLEI; TOTAL CROSS SECTION
MEASUREMENTS ARE NOT INCLUDED [a]

Author	Incident Particle	Energy mev	Nucleus	Parameters Measured
Preston (1960)	p	3,000	H, C	σ
Bareyre (1961)	p	2,000	Be	P
Batty (1959)	p	970	C	σ
Mesheryakov (1957)	p	635	Be	σ, P
Ashmore (1958)	n	350	C, Al	σ
Chamberlain (1956)	p	$\begin{cases} 313 \\ 289 \end{cases}$		σ, P, R
Hafner (1958)	p	220	He, Be, C, N	σ, P
Johannson (1960)	p	160	Li, Be, C, Al	σ, P
Harding (1958)	n	155	C	σ, P
Steinberg (1961) Gerstein (1957) Postma (1961) Cormack (1959)	p	$\begin{cases} 144 \\ 146 \end{cases}$	D, He, Be, C, Al	σ, P
Van Zyl (1956)	n	136	D, Li, Be, C, N, O, Al	σ
Dickson (1957)	p	95	C	σ, P
Taylor (1961)		142	Be, C, N, O, Al	σ
Gerstein (1957)	p	95	C	σ
Salmon (1960)	n	95	Be, C	σ
Bird (1960)	p	140	C, Be, B	R
Hee (1962)	p	139	C	A
Hoffman (1962)	p	139	D	R, A

[a] Reviews of this and other data are given in Glassgold (1959), Taylor (1957), Wilson (1961), Batty (1962), and Faissner (1959) though not always with the same emphasis on small angle scattering.

TABLE 10-2   ABSORPTION CROSS SECTIONS OF NUCLEONS ON
LIGHT NUCLEI

Author	Incident Particle	Energy	Nucleus
DeJuren (1950)	n	95	C, Al
Voss (1956)	n	55–137	C, Al
Ball (1952)	n	310	C, Al
Millburn (1954)	p	290	C
Goloskie (1962)	p	50–150	C, Al
Kirschbaum (1954)	p	190–310	C, Al

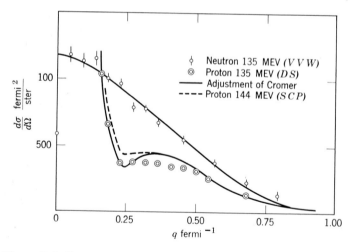

Figure 10-2. Cross section for $P + C$ and $N + C$ at 135 mev versus momentum transfer q. The solid lines are the adjustment of Cromer. The dotted line is an adjustment to fit Steinberg (1961).

The polarization is not so easily interpreted. The value of R remains positive for small angles at both 310 and 140 mev, showing that $H < G$ at these energies. $(1 - R)$ is quadratic in θ showing that H/G is proportional to θ as expected. The polarization parameter P then gives precise numbers.

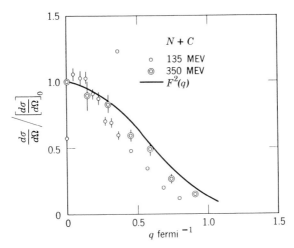

Figure 10-3. Comparison of $N + C$ cross sections at different energies versus q. The solid line is the nuclear form factor derived from electron scattering.

Equation (10-5) shows that if G and H have the same nuclear form factor, P should be independent of element; Figure 10-6 shows that this is indeed true for $qR < 2$; a diffraction dip then commences.

This simple fact is only true if we express all quantities in the *laboratory* system of coordinates. This is clear from the discussion leading to (10-2). By working first in the nucleon-nucleon cm system and then the nucleon-nucleus cm system, most workers complicate their formulae with kinematic factors. Multiple scattering plays an important role in this diffraction dip, and must be calculated with a potential. However, if a simple potential proportional

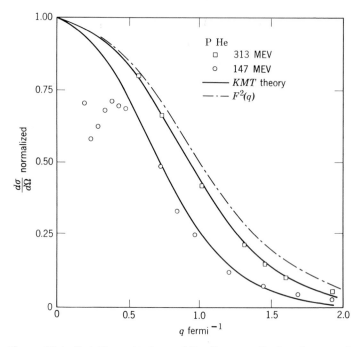

Figure 10-4. $P +$ He scattering, arbitrarily normalized and comparison both with $F^2(q)$ and with calculations of Kerman (1959) (KMT) and the form factor for helium derived from electron scattering.

to $\rho(r)$ is assumed, then calculations fail to fit the data, particularly for helium where P is predicted to be $+1$ in a region where experimentally it is -1. The full potential of equation (10-8) gives good agreement with the data as shown in Figure 10-6.

Table 10-3 compares nuclear amplitudes given by a best fit to the data by Cromer with those from nucleon-nucleon scattering.

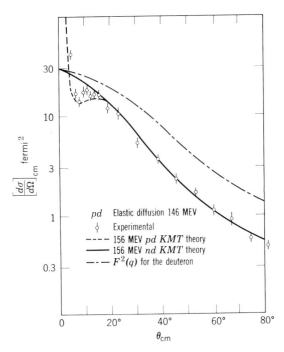

Figure 10-5. $P + D$ scattering at 156 mev versus q, and comparison with $F^2(q)$ and theory of Kerman (1959) (KMT).

The scattering from the deuteron can probably be used to derive parameters of the nucleon-nucleon scattering matrix, because it is a spread out structure compared with the other nuclei and the absorption and correlation effects will be smaller. In particular there exists data on σ, P, R and A. Figures 10-8, 10-9, 10-10 (pages 167–69) show comparisons of P, R and A with calculations

TABLE 10-3   CROMER'S FITS TO NUCLEON-CARBON SCATTERING

| | 310 mev | | 135 mev | 144 mev | 150 mev |
	Exp.	Thy.	Exp.	Exp.	Thy.
$G_R(0)f$	3.4	2.5	6.9	5.0	4.9
$G_I(0)f$	9.4	9.6	7.0	7.0	9.7
$H_R/\theta(0)f/\mathrm{rad}$	(8)	2.1	(−1)	(+1)	−0.5
$H_I/\theta(0)f/\mathrm{rad}$	23	26	10	10	9.2
$a_R^2 f^2$	8	5.4	2.4	2.7	3.0
$a_I^2 f^2$	1.2	1.2	3.3		2.4

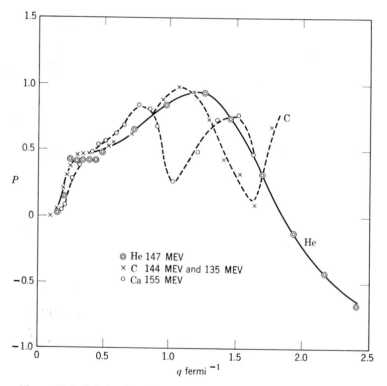

Figure 10-6. Polarization of the proton in scattering from light nuclei.

166

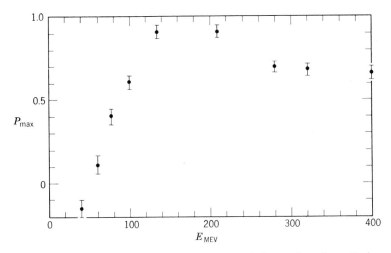

Figure 10-7. The maximum polarization attainable in small angle scattering from carbon as a function of energy.

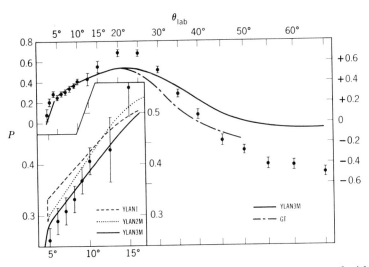

Figure 10-8. Polarization in *pd* elastic scattering at 147 mev compared with various phase shift solutions of Hull (1961) and the potential of Gammel and Thaler.

167

based on the phase shifts YLAN3M of Chapter 7. The scattering amplitudes are the sum of pp and np amplitudes [equation (10-2)]. The np can in turn be expressed as a sum of isotopic singlet and triplet amplitudes. Thus the cross section is determined by

$$\Sigma_t = \bar{A}^2 + \tfrac{2}{3}\bar{B}^2 + \tfrac{5}{3}\bar{C}^2 + \tfrac{2}{3}\bar{E}^2 + \tfrac{2}{3}\bar{F}^2 \qquad (10\text{-}14)$$

with $\bar{A} = \tfrac{3}{4}A_{T=1} + \tfrac{1}{4}A_{T=0} = \tfrac{1}{2}A_{pp} + \tfrac{1}{2}A_{np}$, etc., and similar equations for P, R and A.

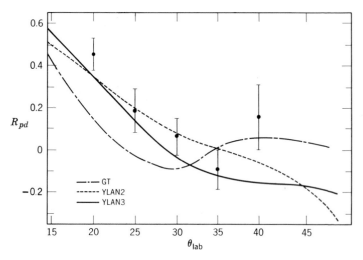

Figure 10-9. The parameter R in pd elastic scattering at 140 mev compared with various phase shift solutions of Hull (1961).

It is worth emphasizing here that the theory only holds for small angles and light elements and that even then the full complication of the potential of equation (10-6) is needed. At larger angles the theory breaks down. It is not our intention to discuss the validity of the optical model for large angles and for heavy elements. Suffice to say that its derivation in terms of nucleon-nucleon scattering parameters is not direct, and the theory is not expected to hold with precision.

In conclusion, therefore, we find qualitative agreement for small angle nucleon scattering from light nuclei. Quantitative agreement must await exact nucleon-nucleon amplitudes, and possibly im-

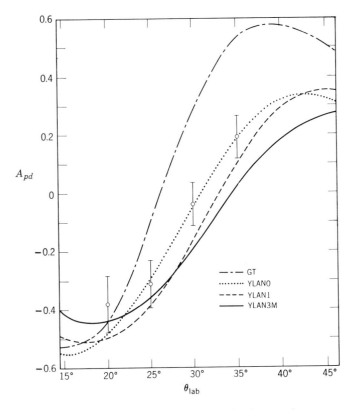

Figure 10-10. The parameter A in pd elastic scattering.

provements in the calculational techniques such as an inclusion of the effect of nucleon correlations. The data of this section is, of course, important in a phenomenological way, for the selection of a polarization analysis for the experiments of Chapter 4 and 5.

Figure 10-7 shows a plot of the maximum polarizational attainable at a given energy.

The fact that the theory is qualitatively correct for incident energies above 60 mev is germane to the subject of finding a polarization analyser for the experiments of Chapters 5 and 6. The requirements for such an analyser are a high cross section, to maintain a high counting rate, and a high polarization. The high cross section suggests that the scattering be at an angle such that $qR < 1$ (less than the first diffraction minimum), where our theory should hold. The nucleon-nucleon amplitudes have little spin dependence at 60 mev, so that polarization analysers are not efficient as Figure 10-7 shows.

Below 60 mev the approximations of this chapter are invalid, and the discussion becomes one of nuclear physics. In particular $p\alpha$ scattering gives high polarizations at 38 mev and large angles (Hwang 1962).

The same calculational procedures may be followed to find the excitation of low-lying excited states of a nucleus, as has been done by Kerman (1959). The cross section depends upon the nucleon-nucleon amplitudes, and the lifetime of the excited state, and the polarization depends primarily on the relative amount of spin-flip in the scattering amplitude. This falls outside the scope of this book.

It is not a very powerful way of finding the lifetime of an excited state. The same parameter can be found with fewer approximations, by exciting the state with electrons (when a similar formula applies). All experiments so far have been confined to verifying that this model—the direct interaction model—is applicable.

Another case of especial interest arises, that of slightly inelastic scattering from the deuteron—where the deuteron appears in a ^1S state. This will be a spin-flip transition, occurring only through the amplitudes B, E and F in (3-6). The analogous reaction for electrons has been discussed in Chapter 8. As was then found, the effects of nuclear forces in the final ^1S state can be calculated and involve the same integral as in equation (8-15) with G_{MV} replaced by a nuclear amplitude Σ_S, assuming we neglect the interaction of the *outgoing* particle with the final state. A square well was used in the calculations, but the momentum transfer is low enough that details of the potential shape should be insignificant. Small contributions from transitions to unbound ^3S states and to the continuum are observed.

We may thus derive the amplitude for the reaction

$$\Sigma_S = \tilde{B}^2 + \tilde{C}^2 + \tilde{E}^2 + \tilde{F}^2 \qquad (10\text{-}15)$$

where $\tilde{B} = B_{T=1} - B_{T=0}$, etc. Figure 10-11 shows the energy distribution of the scattered protons and a fit to theory (Stairs, 1963),

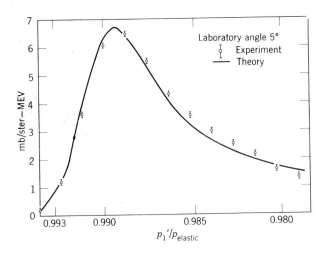

Figure 10-11. Slightly inelastic scattering from the deuteron at 155 mev and a fitted curve. This curve is used to derive the parameter Σ_s in Table 10-4.

and Table 10-4 tabulates the parameters Σ_t and Σ_S derived from the elastic and inelastic scattering, compared with the prediction of the phase shift solution YLAN3M of Hull (1961) discussed in Chapter 7.

TABLE 10-4   PREDICTED (YLAN3M) AND MEASURED VALUES
OF Σ_s AND Σ_t

Lab Angle	Measured		Predicted	
	Σ_s	Σ_t	Σ_s	Σ_t
5°	12.17 ± 0.25	7.82 ± 0.35	10.11	6.29
10°	11.50 ± 0.70	11.52 ± 0.70	8.02	10.89
15°	10.32 ± 0.54	9.79 ± 0.37	6.16	11.32
20°	6.70 ± 0.45	8.59 ± 0.80	4.96	10.11

10.3   Scattering off the Mass Shell

It was noted in the last section that at large q the nucleon-nucleus scattering involved nucleon-nucleon scattering off the mass shell. If the comparison there outlined between theory and experiment could be sufficiently refined, any discrepancy could be interpreted as a measurement of the scattering off the mass shell. An extreme case would seem to be elastic p-p scattering near the pickup peak at 180°. Only tentative attempts have so far been made to analyse this (Postma, 1961, Teem, 1954).

10.4   Effects of Nucleon Correlations

The calculations outlined above neglect the effect of the correlation in position between two nucleons. Various attempts have been made to estimate these.

Firstly for the central potential we derive from equations (10-2) and (10-13)

$$\text{Im } G(0) = (k/4\pi\sigma)_{\text{tot}} = (k/4\pi)[Z\sigma_{np}(\text{tot}) + (A - Z)\sigma_{nn}(\text{tot})]$$

$$(10\text{-}16)$$

a relation between the total cross section for neutron-nucleus scattering and the total cross section for nucleon-nucleon scattering.

This is an obvious relation and it is modified by the multiple scattering processes to give [see equation (10-9)]

$$\int_0^\infty V_I dr = (k/4\pi)[Z\sigma_{np} + (A - Z)\sigma_{nn}] \qquad (10\text{-}17)$$

The physical meaning of these equations is at once apparent. We merely *add* the total cross sections, and apply a simple correction (via a potential) for the eclipsing of some nucleons by the others. If, however, we consider the details of the processes, we find that this cannot be true below 400 mev, for nuclei of helium and higher A. Most np collisions are at small or large angles (Figures 6-2 and 3) and the recoil particle is then of a low energy, *too low* to escape from the potential well binding the nucleons. Since the energy states of a nucleon are all filled, these scatterings are inhibited, and V_I is *less* than given by equation (10-15). At higher energies (>300 mev) where this effect is small, another comes into play. In deriving equation (10-8) we assume that the distribution of nucleons throughout the nucleus is uniform. In fact it is not; two nucleons are not allowed to be too close because of the exclusion principle. The eclipsing corrections become greater and V_I is *greater* than given by equation (10-15). These corrections have been extensively discussed (Glauber, 1956, Dabrowski, 1959, 1961).

The effect of nucleon correlations on Re $G(\theta)$ is not so obvious. Dabrowski (1961) suggest that Re $G(\theta)$ should be increased thereby. Such an increase is suggested by the neutron scattering data at 95 and 135 mev (Salmon, 1960, Van Zyl, 1956, Wilson, 1959).

The effect of nucleon correlations seems particularly marked for He⁴. Kerman (1959) and Cormack (1959) both comment that the theory seems to give a scattering too large by a factor of two, although the qualitative features about the increase of radii given by equation (10-11) are still given correctly. Herzenberg (1960) attributes this to the correlations and obtains reasonable agreement.

In principle it seems that it should be possible to derive directly information on the two nucleon correlation function. This has not yet been done.

Chapter 11

Present Status

It can now be confidently stated that there are unique values for the $T = 1$ phase shifts from 0 to 300 mev from *pp* scattering (Table 7-3). The accuracy is not all that may be desired, however. In the laboratory energy range of 20 to 100 mev triple scattering experiments are scarce and would yield precise values. Since this is an energy region in which the $^3P_0$ phase, for example, has a maximum, the details may be interesting.

It is possible that by assuming charge independence, the same uniqueness is true for the *np* system as well. The work of Hull (1961) and Kazarinov (1962) strongly suggests this. A few more *np* triple scattering experiments should decide this question.

Specifically the following experiments seem ripe for improvement. At low energies, the total *np* cross section should be remeasured, and the C^{13} coherent and total cross sections to correct the *np* coherent cross section measurements. A precise $\frac{1}{2}\%$ measurement of the cross section for photodisintegration of the deuteron at a few mev can confirm the triplet shape parameter.

Above 20 mev, the most useful quantities are the correlation coefficients which can directly separate singlet and triplet states. It may be experimentally easier to measure the triple scattering parameters around 60 mev which is at the moment the most interesting region. *np* triple scattering measurements are also needed.

For radiative processes, precise measurements of the photodisintegration of the deuteron from 20–100 mev are needed, including particularly the extreme angles $0°$ and $180°$.

175

Any measurement which gives an unambiguous result for off-mass shell matrix elements is much needed.

The analysis of the data is not in such a happy state. Phenomenological potentials have been suggested to correlate the data of which perhaps the best is that of Hamada (1962). The interaction region at large distances can be successfully described by a one pion exchange potential with the correct pion nucleon coupling constant, both in np and pp states. The inner region remains a mystery, which has yet to be cleared up. The respective roles of the vector bosons, and uncorrelated two pion states seems obscure, with apparently conflicting claims that the data can be understood with either. The meaning of the repulsive core is still far from clear, though it, and the spin-orbit potential *may* be the effect of vector bosons.

The confirmation, from the photodisintegration of the deuteron, of the large (7%) D state is the only contribution to our understanding from radiative processes. So far the parameters of the nuclear force problem have been used to derive nucleon form factors from electron-deuteron scattering rather than the other way around. The whole of the nuclear force problem is discussed only in a semi-relativistic way. The effective ranges and phase shifts are relativistically covariant quantities but as soon as they are used to discuss other processes, such as elastic electron-deuteron scattering, they are discussed in a nonrelativistic framework. We can notice several anomalies which probably have a common solution in this unsolved problem: The failure of the magnetic moments of the proton, neutron, and deuteron to yield the D state probability in accordance with equation (2-64); the inability to understand the ratio of deuterium to hydrogen hyperfine structure [equation (2-65)]; the failure to predict the np capture cross section [equation (2-49)] and Table 2-8]; the failure to understand the precise electron-deuteron elastic scattering in terms of the theory of Chapter 8.

Charge independence still can be further checked by precise nn scattering measurements, using, perhaps, the theory of the deuteron. It would be interesting to measure the small (10^{-7}) parity nonconserving term predicted in Chapter 9.

Experimental Numbers for Nucleon-Nucleon Scattering

In this appendix are listed all experimental numbers which it is believed are useful in nucleon-nucleon scattering. Following the usual conventions, the angles and cross sections are in the cm. system, but the energy is in the lab. system.

Numbers excluded are low energy parameters already listed in Chapter 2 (Table 2-10); the pp correlation parameters listed in Table 5-5; data which have been superseded by more precise data; antiproton-proton scattering data; meson production and inelastic scattering generally; data from radiative processes. If other data are excluded, it is because of the author's incompetence.

The data are presented in a form for use in computer calculations. Thus the np differential cross section data, though normalized in tables, usually have an arbitrary normalization factor. The normalization is achieved by using the total cross section data and is best left to the computer. pp cross sections have a normalization factor for all cross sections at the same energy. This is listed with its error under "absolute error." In general, the systematic errors in energy determination and normalization are common to all points at the same energy and the same authors. For fuller details consult the papers concerned. For earlier data consult the compilation of Hess (1958).

TABLE A-1 pp TOTAL CROSS SECTIONS

Author	$\int_{\theta \, min}^{\pi/2} d\sigma$ millibarns	θ min [a] cm.	E mev
Golaskie (1962)	38.7 ± 0.5	$12°$	69.8
	32.8 ± 0.4	$12°$	90.7
	28.3 ± 0.3	$12°$	108
	25.9 ± 0.2	$12°$	122
	24.9 ± 0.2	$12°$	134
	23.7 ± 0.2	$12°$	147
Taylor (1956)	23.7 ± 0.9	$0°$	134
Chamberlain (1954)	21.3 ± 0.7	$20°$	225
	22.2 ± 0.7		330
Dzelephov (1955)	26.9 ± 0.7	$0°$	410
	27.6 ± 0.4	$0°$	460
	29.9 ± 0.4	$0°$	500
	32.1 ± 0.5	$0°$	540
	35.6 ± 0.5	$0°$	580
	36.6 ± 0.5	$0°$	600
	38.6 ± 0.5	$0°$	620
	39.8 ± 0.6	$0°$	640
	41.4 ± 0.6	$0°$	660
Chen (1956)	26.5 ± 1.4	$0°$	410
	29.8 ± 1.2	$0°$	535
	37.7 ± 1.4	$0°$	615
	44.4 ± 2.8	$0°$	740
	47.8 ± 1.6	$0°$	830
	47.6 ± 1.7	$0°$	850
	48.3 ± 1.6	$0°$	1075
	47.5 ± 1.6	$0°$	1275
	49.4 ± 1.6	$0°$	1295
	47.2 ± 2.6	$0°$	1490
	41.4 ± 3.2	$0°$	2000
	41.6 ± 4.0	$0°$	2600
Law (1959)	46.1 ± 0.5	$0°$	1010
Longo (1960)	46.9 ± 1.0	$0°$	1.40 [b]
	47.5 ± 2.2	$0°$	1.46
	47.7 ± 3.0	$0°$	1.60
	46.5 ± 2.0	$0°$	1.73
	46.3 ± 3.2	$0°$	1.89
	45.0 ± 3.0	$0°$	2.05
	45.6 ± 1.9	$0°$	2.47
	45.1 ± 0.9	$0°$	2.97
	43.3 ± 0.6	$0°$	3.58
	42.4 ± 0.6	$0°$	4.00
Von Dardel (1961) Lindenbaum (1961) Ashmore (1960) Diddens (1962)	Numbers are not available. A comparison graph is plotted in Diddens (1962).		

[a] When θ min $= 0$. An extrapolation has been made to zero by a plausible curve to exclude Coulomb effects.

[b] These are momenta in Bev/c, not energies.

TABLE A-2 *pp* DIFFERENTIAL CROSS SECTIONS

Author, Energy, Absolute Error (in %)	θ cm.	$d\sigma/d\Omega$ millibarns/ster. (relative)
Cork (1954)	27°32′	55.95 ± 0.23
9.73 mev	40°16′	52.46 ± 0.10
Abs. error	49°48′	53.89 ± 0.31
1 ± 0.008	59°38′	55.06 ± 0.22
	60°8′	55.38 ± 0.40
	68°20′	54.84 ± 0.24
	79°44′	53.91 ± 0.20
	90°50′	56.11 ± 0.23
	112°35′	54.52 ± 0.58
Johnston (1959)	10.026	854.9 ± 1.7
9.69 mev	12.031	400.2 ± 1.0
Abs. error	14.035	219.2 ± 0.8
1 ± 0.005	16.041	138.8 ± 0.7
Error in %	18.046	95.8 ± 0.7
	20.051	75.5 ± 0.7
	22.055	64.4 ± 0.7
	24.060	58.1 ± 0.7
	26.064	54.7 ± 0.7
	28.069	53.1 ± 0.7
	30.074	51.8 ± 0.7
	32.079	51.8 ± 0.7
	34.083	51.4 ± 0.7
	36.087	51.0 ± 0.7
	38.091	51.7 ± 0.7
	40.096	51.4 ± 0.7
	44.103	52.6 ± 0.7
	50.113	53.1 ± 0.7
	54.120	53.2 ± 0.7
	60.128	53.9 ± 0.7
	64.133	54.05 ± 0.7
	70.139	54.1 ± 0.7
	76.144	54.4 ± 0.7
	80.145	54.4 ± 0.7
	86.148	54.3 ± 0.7
	90.148	54.6 ± 0.7

TABLE A-2   (*Continued*)

Author, Energy, Absolute Error	θ cm.	$d\sigma/d\Omega$ millibarns/ster. (relative)
Yntema (1954)	90	27.32 ± 0.14
18.2 mev	80	27.29 ± 0.14
Abs. error	70	27.46 ± 0.14
1 ± 0.005	60	27.42 ± 0.16
	50	27.27 ± 0.19
	40	26.55 ± 0.21
	36	26.00 ± 0.26
	30	24.94 ± 0.25
Jeong (1960)	10.07	109.6 ± 1.8
25.63 mev	12.08	56.31 ± 1.1
Abs. error	14.09	33.20 ± 0.6
1 ± 0.005	16.11	23.76 ± 0.5
Error in %	18.12	19.90 ± 0.5
	19.13	18.70 ± 0.5
	20.13	17.98 ± 0.5
	22.15	17.33 ± 0.5
	24.16	17.09 ± 0.5
	25.16	17.16 ± 0.5
	26.17	17.17 ± 0.5
	28.18	17.30 ± 0.5
	30.19	17.43 ± 0.5
	32.21	17.68 ± 0.5
	34.22	17.80 ± 0.5
	36.23	17.93 ± 0.5
	40.25	18.20 ± 0.5
	44.27	18.33 ± 0.5
	50.30	18.52 ± 0.5
	60.34	18.56 ± 0.5
	70.37	18.65 ± 0.5
	80.38	18.60 ± 0.5
	90.39	18.59 ± 0.5
Johnston (1958)	8°5′	103.8 ± 4.0
39.4 mev	10°6′	40.85 ± 1.7
Abs. error	12°7′	20.63 ± 0.9
1 ± 0.005	14°9′	13.50 ± 0.6
Error in %	16°10′	10.87 ± 0.5
	17°11′	10.26 ± 0.5

TABLE A-2 *(Continued)*

Author, Energy, Absolute Error	θ cm.	$d\sigma/d\Omega$ millibarns/ster. (relative)
Error in %	18°11′	10.01 ± 0.5
	19°12′	9.98 ± 0.5
	20°12′	9.79 ± 0.5
	21°13′	9.82 ± 0.5
	22°14′	9.85 ± 0.5
	23°14′	9.93 ± 0.5
	24°15′	9.94 ± 0.5
	25°15′	10.07 ± 0.5
	27°16′	10.27 ± 0.5
	30°18′	10.52 ± 0.5
	36°21′	10.75 ± 0.5
	40°23′	10.86 ± 0.5
	44°25′	10.98 ± 0.5
	50°27′	11.10 ± 0.5
	56°30′	11.13 ± 0.5
	60°31′	11.16 ± 0.5
	64°32′	11.18 ± 0.5
	70°34′	11.17 ± 0.5
	76°35′	11.18 ± 0.5
	80°35′	11.16 ± 0.5
	90°36′	11.16 ± 0.5
Young (1960) Quoted error absolute in %		
68.4 mev	90°	6.13 ± 1.1
62.0 mev	90°	6.76 ± 1.1
56.2 mev	90°	7.45 ± 1.1
50.2 mev	90°	8.40 ± 1.1
44.7 mev	90°	9.51 ± 1.1
39.6 mev	90°	11.19 ± 1.0
36.9 mev	90°	12.14 ± 1.0
34.2 mev	90°	13.36 ± 1.0
31.1 mev	90°	14.68 ± 1.0
28.2 mev	90°	16.27 ± 1.3
9.7 mev	90°	54.6 ± 0.7

TABLE A-2   (*Continued*)

Author, Energy, Absolute Error	θ cm.	$d\sigma/d\Omega$ millibarns/ster. (relative)
Young (1960)	10.18	12.84 ± 1.7
68.30 mev	12.21	7.05 ± 0.9
Abs. error	13.23	6.14 ± 0.8
1 ± 0.008	14.25	5.53 ± 0.6
Error in %	16.28	5.19 ± 0.5
	18.32	5.23 ± 0.5
	20.35	5.50 ± 0.5
	22.39	5.66 ± 0.5
	24.42	5.81 ± 0.5
	26.45	5.94 ± 0.5
	28.48	6.11 ± 0.5
	30.52	6.23 ± 0.5
	32.55	6.28 ± 0.5
	34.58	6.33 ± 0.5
	36.61	6.30 ± 0.5
	40.66	6.34 ± 0.5
	44.72	6.30 ± 0.5
	50.79	6.32 ± 0.5
	54.83	6.30 ± 0.5
	60.89	6.34 ± 0.5
	64.92	6.29 ± 0.5
	70.97	6.21 ± 0.5
	74.98	6.16 ± 0.5
	81.01	6.17 ± 0.5
	91.02	6.16 ± 0.5
	101.01	6.16 ± 0.5
Kruse (1956)	25	4.75 ± 0.20
Abs. error	30	4.75 ± 0.20
1 ± 0.03	35	4.75 ± 0.20
95 mev	40	4.83 ± 0.10
	50	4.81 ± 0.10
	60	4.75 ± 0.10
	70	4.68 ± 0.13
	80	4.58 ± 0.10
	90	4.54 ± 0.10

TABLE A-2   *(Continued)*

Author, Energy, Absolute Error	θ cm.	$d\sigma/d\Omega$ millibarns/ster. (relative)
Kruse (1956)		
78.5 mev	90	5.40 ± 0.32
69.5 mev	90	5.96 ± 0.36
52 mev	90	8.83 ± 0.62
41 mev	90	11.4 ± 0.80
Absolute		
Taylor (1959)	10.2	12.40 ± 0.30
98 mev	12.3	5.23 ± 0.13
Abs. error	14.3	3.53 ± 0.10
1 ± 0.05	16.4	3.28 ± 0.08
	18.5	3.28 ± 0.08
	20.5	3.68 ± 0.08
	22.6	3.79 ± 0.07
	25.6	4.00 ± 0.08
	30.7	4.10 ± 0.08
	40.9	4.41 ± 0.10
	51.1	4.46 ± 0.10
	61.3	4.45 ± 0.10
	71.4	4.46 ± 0.10
	81.4	4.39 ± 0.10
Taylor (1959)	5.19	69.24 ± 2.6
142 mev	6.23	28.77 ± 0.59
Abs. error	7.27	12.96 ± 0.43
1 ± 0.05	8.30	7.75 ± 0.28
Several runs inde-	8.82	5.76 ± 0.30
pendently nor-	9.34	4.91 ± 0.25
malized	10.38	4.44 ± 0.04
	12.46	3.50 ± 0.06
	14.53	3.44 ± 0.05
	16.61	3.56 ± 0.05
	20.76	3.66 ± 0.04
	25.95	3.79 ± 0.05
	31.06	3.85 ± 0.05
	37.20	4.05 ± 0.06
	41.34	3.86 ± 0.04

TABLE A-2   (*Continued*)

Author, Energy, Absolute Error	θ cm.	$d\sigma/d\Omega$ millibarns/ster. (relative)
	51.62	3.96 ± 0.07
	61.84	3.90 ± 0.07
	71.98	4.00 ± 0.07
	82.06	4.02 ± 0.07
	90.00	4.08 ± 0.07
Palmieri (1958)	20.6	4.09 ± 0.08
95 mev	25.7	4.51 ± 0.08
To be taken as rel-	30.7	4.71 ± 0.08
ative only	35.8	4.77 ± 0.08
	40.9	4.68 ± 0.08
	46.0	4.74 ± 0.08
	51.1	4.74 ± 0.08
	56.2	4.66 ± 0.08
	61.2	4.64 ± 0.08
	66.3	4.63 ± 0.08
	71.3	4.61 ± 0.08
	76.4	4.58 ± 0.08
	81.4	4.51 ± 0.08
	86.4	4.46 ± 0.08
102 mev	30.8	4.50 ± 0.08
Relative only	46.1	4.50 ± 0.08
	66.4	4.62 ± 0.08
118 mev	20.6	3.63 ± 0.06
Relative only	25.8	3.99 ± 0.06
	30.9	4.07 ± 0.06
	36.0	4.13 ± 0.06
	41.1	4.12 ± 0.06
	46.2	4.08 ± 0.06
	51.4	4.05 ± 0.06
	56.5	4.04 ± 0.06
	61.5	3.92 ± 0.06
	66.6	3.97 ± 0.06
	71.7	3.91 ± 0.06
	76.7	4.02 ± 0.06
	81.7	4.00 ± 0.06

TABLE A-2 *(Continued)*

Author, Energy, Absolute Error	θ cm.	$d\sigma/d\Omega$ millibarns/ster. (relative)
	86.8	4.11 ± 0.06
	91.8	4.02 ± 0.06
	96.7	3.97 ± 0.06
Palmieri (1958)	6.20	27.70 ± 0.73
Relative only	8.34	8.10 ± 0.20
147 ± 1 mev [a]	10.4	4.55 ± 0.11
	12.4	3.79 ± 0.10
	14.5	3.88 ± 0.10
	16.6	4.02 ± 0.10
	18.7	4.03 ± 0.10
	20.7	4.15 ± 0.10
	22.8	4.14 ± 0.11
	24.9	4.26 ± 0.11
	31.1	4.22 ± 0.11
Palmieri (1958)	20.7	4.17 ± 0.08
Relative only	25.9	4.29 ± 0.08
147 ± 1 mev [a]	31.1	4.39 ± 0.08
	36.3	4.31 ± 0.08
	41.4	4.21 ± 0.04
	46.5	4.21 ± 0.04
	51.7	4.16 ± 0.04
	56.8	4.14 ± 0.04
	61.9	4.12 ± 0.04
	67.0	4.12 ± 0.04
	72.0	4.07 ± 0.04
	77.1	4.06 ± 0.05
	82.1	4.07 ± 0.05
	87.2	4.11 ± 0.05
	92.2	4.12 ± 0.05
	97.1	4.13 ± 0.05
	102.1	4.12 ± 0.05
	107.1	4.14 ± 0.05
	112.0	4.09 ± 0.05

[a] Palmieri's two sets of data at 147 mev have separate normalizations.

TABLE A-2   (*Continued*)

Author, Energy, Absolute Error	θ cm.	$d\sigma/d\Omega$ millibarns/ster. (relative)
Tinlot (1962)	30°	3.80 ± 0.06
Abs. error	40°	3.83 ± 0.05
1 ± 0.1	50°	3.73 ± 0.04
213 mev	60°	3.65 ± 0.04
	70°	3.66 ± 0.04
	80°	3.66 ± 0.03
	90°	3.61 ± 0.04
Caversazio (1961)	8°3′	8.48 ± 0.25
156 mev	10°4′	3.95 ± 0.09
Abs. error	12°5′	3.37 ± 0.09
1 ± 0.04	14°5′	3.30 ± 0.13
	16°8′	3.35 ± 0.13
	18°7′	3.49 ± 0.14
	20°8′	3.66 ± 0.14
	22°9′	3.87 ± 0.07
	25°	3.58 ± 0.06
	26°	3.62 ± 0.06
	27°	3.84 ± 0.06
	29°	3.75 ± 0.06
	31°1′	3.87 ± 0.05
	35°5′	3.85 ± 0.05
	37°3′	3.74 ± 0.09
	41°5′	3.88 ± 0.05
	46°6′	3.83 ± 0.05
	51°7′	3.82 ± 0.05
	62°	3.70 ± 0.04
	72°	3.71 ± 0.04
	82°2′	3.67 ± 0.04
	90°2′	3.71 ± 0.06
	102°2′	3.75 ± 0.06
	112°	3.76 ± 0.06
Chamberlain (1957)	35.6	4.31 ± 0.21
345 mev	36.4	3.93 ± 0.15
Abs. error	43.4	3.79 ± 0.15
1 ± 0.05	44.0	4.17 ± 0.13

TABLE A-2 *(Continued)*

Author, Energy, Absolute Error	θ cm.	$d\sigma/d\Omega$ millibarns/ster. (relative)
	45.8	3.64 ± 0.07
	46.1	3.99 ± 0.11
	52.4	3.77 ± 0.10
	60.8	3.83 ± 0.13
	64.0	3.55 ± 0.11
	64.0	3.74 ± 0.14
	70.6	3.67 ± 0.16
	72.2	3.67 ± 0.11
	80.2	3.95 ± 0.12
	87.6	3.86 ± 0.10
	88.2	3.91 ± 0.08
	88.2	3.70 ± 0.08
	88.6	3.85 ± 0.06
	88.6	3.54 ± 0.09
	89.2	4.15 ± 0.36
	11.3	5.1 ± 0.36
	11.3	5.38 ± 0.49
	15.2	3.71 ± 0.22
	15.2	3.21 ± 0.17
	21.1	3.51 ± 0.10
	21.7	3.06 ± 0.15
	32.5	3.52 ± 0.09
	33.1	3.51 ± 0.11
	42.8	3.48 ± 0.10
	42.8	3.40 ± 0.08
	53.2	3.40 ± 0.08
	53.2	3.28 ± 0.10
Fischer (1954)	4.67	35.7 ± 2.3
330 mev	5.26	18.1 ± 1.02
Relative only	5.88	14.62 ± 1.02
	6.52	8.59 ± 0.82
	7.28	6.34 ± 0.61
	8.57	4.15 ± 0.33
	9.20	3.62 ± 0.31
	10.16	3.29 ± 0.33

TABLE A-2   (*Continued*)

Author, Energy, Absolute Error	θ cm.	$d\sigma/d\Omega$ millibarns/ster. (relative)
	11.12	4.56 ± 0.25
	11.43	3.14 ± 0.36
	12.93	3.45 ± 0.31
	14.80	3.49 ± 0.29
	16.77	3.58 ± 0.23
	18.63	3.44 ± 0.27
	20.87	4.02 ± 0.24
	22.80	3.62 ± 0.29
	24.27	3.75 ± 0.31
	26.03	3.66 ± 0.31
	27.57	3.63 ± 0.35
	29.70	3.81 ± 0.35
Holt (1958)	4.14	26.40 ± 1.19
Abs error	4.69	15.90 ± 0.68
1 ± 0.02	5.28	11.47 ± 0.48
380 mev	6.42	6.63 ± 0.20
	7.56	5.31 ± 0.15
	8.73	4.57 ± 0.10
	9.9	4.35 ± 0.10
	11.0	4.35 ± 0.08
	12.1	4.34 ± 0.10
	13.2	4.31 ± 0.06
	14.3	4.35 ± 0.08
	15.4	4.26 ± 0.07
	16.5	4.27 ± 0.06
	17.6	4.27 ± 0.06
	19.8	4.20 ± 0.07
	21.8	4.22 ± 0.07
	24.0	4.12 ± 0.07
	26.2	4.18 ± 0.07
	28.4	4.08 ± 0.07
	30.0	4.04 ± 0.07
	30.6	4.01 ± 0.07
	36.0	4.04 ± 0.08
	43.0	4.01 ± 0.08

TABLE A-2 *(Continued)*

Author, Energy, Absolute Error	θ cm.	$d\sigma/d\Omega$ millibarns/ster. (relative)
	50.0	3.86 ± 0.07
	65.0	3.76 ± 0.07
	90.0	3.70 ± 0.06
Sutton (1955)	17	4.13 ± 0.14
437 mev	25	4.27 ± 0.10
Abs. error	28	4.04 ± 0.13
1 ± 0.03	30	4.03 ± 0.06
	36	4.05 ± 0.04
	50	3.82 ± 0.06
	65	3.62 ± 0.06
	90	3.49 ± 0.05
Mescheriakov (1954, 1955)	5	33 ± 6
	10	5.91 ± 0.46
460 mev	15	4.69 ± 0.38
	20	3.98 ± 0.56
	27	3.73 ± 0.34
	33	3.97 ± 0.16
	40	4.06 ± 0.16
	46	3.99 ± 0.12
	53	3.84 ± 0.14
	55	3.36 ± 0.25
	66	3.82 ± 0.14
	78	3.52 ± 0.14
	90	3.50 ± 0.10
	55	3.59 ± 0.21
	66	3.81 ± 0.18
	78	3.56 ± 0.20
	90	3.31 ± 0.15
Mescheriakov (1954, 1955)		
510 mev	90	3.20 ± 0.18
562 mev	90	2.95 ± 0.12
586 mev	90	2.92 ± 0.11
610 mev	90	2.63 ± 0.10

TABLE A-2   (*Continued*)

Author, Energy, Absolute Error	θ cm.	$d\sigma/d\Omega$ millibarns/ster. (relative)
622 mev	90	2.58 ± 0.12
634 mev	90	2.30 ± 0.10
645 mev	90	2.20 ± 0.10
657 mev	90	2.05 ± 0.07
460 mev	30	4.18 ± 0.44
562 mev	30	4.93 ± 0.29
610 mev	30	5.67 ± 0.26
634 mev	30	6.37 ± 0.36
645 mev	30	6.53 ± 0.37
657 mev	30	6.55 ± 0.28
Selektor (1954)		
460 mev	30	3.58 ± 0.31
	45	3.89 ± 0.09
	60	3.82 ± 0.09
	75	3.60 ± 0.12
	90	3.68 ± 0.09
560 mev	40	4.32 ± 0.14
	60	3.66 ± 0.19
	75	3.28 ± 0.14
	90	3.22 ± 0.13
660 mev	30	5.47 ± 0.12
	40	4.97 ± 0.10
	50	4.03 ± 0.12
	60	3.21 ± 0.12
	70	2.59 ± 0.10
	80	2.19 ± 0.11
	90	2.06 ± 0.08
Bogachev (1954, 1955, 1958)		
460 mev	5	33 ± 6
	10	5.91 ± 0.46
	15	4.69 ± 0.38
560 mev	5	26 ± 5
	10	8.04 ± 0.78
	15	6.78 ± 0.63

TABLE A-2   (*Continued*)

Author, Energy, Absolute Error	θ cm.	$d\sigma/d\Omega$ millibarns/ster. (relative)
	20	6.29 ± 0.58
	25	5.70 ± 0.53
660 mev	5	18.9 ± 1.1
	10	11.0 ± 0.7
	15	8.67 ± 0.53
	20	7.75 ± 0.48
	25	6.56 ± 0.40
657 mev	30	5.58 ± 0.15
	40	4.78 ± 0.26
	50	3.99 ± 0.20
	60	3.41 ± 0.13
	70	2.94 ± 0.12
	80	2.20 ± 0.05
	90	2.07 ± 0.03
Bogomolov (1956)		
660 mev	7.5	17.32 ± 1.85
	10	14.98 ± 0.60
	16	7.80 ± 0.49
	20	6.75 ± 0.29
	25	5.79 ± 0.41
	30	5.47 ± 0.29
Smith (1955)		
440 mev	33.2	3.86
Normalized at 440	44.0	3.80
mev to Sutton	65.4	3.62
	79.9	3.52
	90.0	3.49
590 mev	27.5	6.12 ± 0.15
	34.7	5.42 ± 0.10
	50.0	4.18 ± 0.7
	65.1	3.28 ± 0.10
	90.0	2.43 ± 0.05
800 mev	28.5	7.60 ± 0.20
	49.8	3.44 ± 0.10
	90.0	0.89 ± 0.05

TABLE A-2 (*Continued*)

Author, Energy, Absolute Error	θ cm.	$d\sigma/d\Omega$ millibarns/ster. (relative)
1000 mev	36.5	5.66 ± 0.10
	41.3	4.54 ± 0.10
	53.7	2.44 ± 0.07
	64.0	1.33 ± 0.05
	77.0	0.79 ± 0.05
	90.0	0.62 ± 0.05
McFarlane (1963)	12.3	19.6 ± 1.2
970 mev	48.3	3.51 ± 0.09
Absolute	59.7	2.04 ± 0.07
	70.8	1.19 ± 0.04
	81.6	0.90 ± 0.02
Dowell (1960)	18°30′	11.80 ± 0.26
1010 $\pm$ 20 mev	24°36′	10.40 ± 0.33
Normalized at 0°	30°42′	7.89 ± 0.18
by incorrect as-	36°42′	5.76 ± 0.09
sumption of op-	41°30′	4.11 ± 0.09
tical theorem	48°30′	2.718 ± 0.051
	60°0′	1.546 ± 0.041
	71°6′	0.922 ± 0.029
	79°48′	0.739 ± 0.037
	90°0′	0.608 ± 0.030
Preston (1960)	0.50	1.60 ± 0.18
3 Bev	0.61	0.89 ± 0.10
Abs. error	0.68	0.82 ± 0.10
1 $\pm$ 0.05	0.88	0.66 ± 0.08
Lab. angles and	1.08	0.61 ± 0.07
cross sections	1.42	0.49 ± 0.06
in barns/ster.	1.82	0.58 ± 0.06
	1.91	0.42 ± 0.05
	2.30	0.39 ± 0.04
	2.80	0.32 ± 0.03
	3.20	0.35 ± 0.04
	3.68	0.30 ± 0.03
	4.18	0.28 ± 0.03

TABLE A-2   (*Continued*)

Author, Energy, Absolute Error	θ cm.	$d\sigma/d\Omega$ millibarns/ster. (relative)
	0.79	0.66 ± 0.08
	1.40	0.53 ± 0.06
	1.82	0.44 ± 0.05
	2.30	0.45 ± 0.05
	3.68	0.32 ± 0.03
Fujii (1962)	6.2	22.4 ± 1.6
1350 mev	8.9	21.5 ± 1.5
Abs. error	21.2	13.2 ± 0.9
1 ± 0.06	31.1	8.1 ± 0.6
	44.5	2.7 ± 0.2
2100 mev	7.9	28.9 ± 2.0
Abs. error	12.1	24.6 ± 1.7
1 ± 0.06	24.2	10.4 ± 0.7
	34.2	3.0 ± 0.2
	48.8	0.72 ± 0.05
2900 mev	8.6	8.5 ± 2.7
Abs. error	14.3	24.1 ± 1.7
1 ± 0.06	26.8	4.6 ± 0.3
	37.8	1.1 ± 0.1
	54.1	0.227 ± 0.016
Cork (1957)		
2240 mev	14.7	20.8 ± 1.2
Abs. error	23.6	11.0 ± 0.6
1 ± 0.15	29.2	6.64 ± 0.61
	44.0	1.12 ± 0.098
	57.6	0.428 ± 0.060
	70.3	0.255 ± 0.034
	93.5	0.1445 ± 0.0280
3490 mev	34.2	1.7
	49.2	0.26
	64.4	0.07
	78.5	0.06
4400 mev	10.6	20.5 ± 1.1
Abs. error	14.2	18.3 ± 1.4
1 ± 0.15	17.5	12.73 ± 0.90

TABLE A-2   (*Continued*)

Author, Energy, Absolute Error	θ cm.	$d\sigma/d\Omega$ millibarns/ster. (relative)
	21.3	6.01 ± 0.52
	24.5	2.96 ± 0.33
	28.5	1.99 ± 0.23
	37.4	0.473 ± 0.063
	53.2	0.100 ± 0.029
	69.0	0.038 ± 0.015
6150 mev	7.6	27.7 ± 2.8
Abs. error	11.6	24.6 ± 2.2
1 ± 0.15	15.2	10.1 ± 1.3
	20.0	5.51 ± 1.10
	20.8	3.06 ± 0.70
	23.6	1.31 ± 0.31
	27.6	0.65 ± 0.29
Diddens (1962)		
Bev/c		Error in %
12.99	17.5	45 ± 50
15.89	19.2	10 ± 50
17.30	20.0	4.4 ± 50
17.75	20.2	5.3 ± 50
18.69	20.7	1.5 ± 50
19.56	21.2	0.53 ± 50
19.75	21.3	0.90 ± 50
19.91	21.4	0.54 ± 50
21.88	22.3	0.28 ± 50
22.74	22.6	0.24 ± 50
26.02	24.2	0.10 ± 50
18.29	21.9	0.56 ± 50
27.83	26.6	0.026 ± 50
8.94	28.4	2.75 ± 59
11.28	31.5	0.31 ± 50
13.98	34.6	0.12 ± 50
15.96	36.7	0.040 ± 50
18.97	39.5	0.0055 ± 50
21.46	41.8	0.0011 ± 50
22.92	43.0	0.0007 ± 50

TABLE A-2 (*Continued*)

Author, Energy, Absolute Error	θ cm.	$d\sigma/d\Omega$ millibarns/ster. (relative)
Diddens (1962)		Error in %
12.1	2.66	146 ± 11
Bev/c	5.73	96 ± 8
	8.72	45 ± 5
	11.75	21.3 ± 5
	14.7	5.9 ± 6
15.5	3.02	165 ± 12
Bev/c	6.40	76 ± 10
	9.71	27 ± 6
	13.25	6.4 ± 8
	16.50	1.1 ± 15
18.6	3.82	209 ± 12
Bev/c	7.30	66 ± 6
	10.7	12.6 ± 6
	14.4	1.6 ± 15
	17.8	0.25 ± 20
21.4	3.29	182 ± 12
Bev/c	7.30	43 ± 8
	11.18	6.4 ± 7
	15.30	0.52 ± 10
	19.0	0.045 ± 30
26.2	4.21	189 ± 13
Bev/c	8.60	22 ± 7
	12.88	1.24 ± 10
	17.03	0.075 ± 20

TABLE A-3   *pp* POLARIZATIONS

Author, Energy	θ cm.	Polarization
Alexeff (1960)	30	0.0007 ± 0.0016
3.3 mev	45	0.0025 ± 0.0016
	53	0.0058 ± 0.0024
Blanpied (1959) 16.2 mev	50	0.006 ± 0.005
Batty (1962)		
30 mev	45	0.0004 ± 0.0033
50 mev	45	0.0316 ± 0.0017
Christmas (1961)		
27 mev	45	0.0031 ± 0.0046
37.6 mev	45	0.0081 ± 0.0033
37 mev	60	0.0116 ± 0.0033
37 mev	70	0.0108 ± 0.0049
51 mev	45	0.0255 ± 0.0025
52 mev	60	0.0431 ± 0.0102
52 mev	75	0.0080 ± 0.0086
59 mev	45	0.0431 ± 0.0105
70 mev	45	0.0650 ± 0.0065
97 mev	45	0.1252 ± 0.0059
Palmieri (1958)		
46 mev	45.5	0.012 ± 0.013
56 mev	45.5	0.046 ± 0.006
66 mev	20.4	0.050 ± 0.014
Abs. error	25.5	0.047 ± 0.009
1 ± 0.03	30.5	0.077 ± 0.010
	35.6	0.078 ± 0.008
	40.7	0.062 ± 0.008
	45.7	0.069 ± 0.008
	50.8	0.067 ± 0.008
	55.9	0.059 ± 0.008
	60.9	0.058 ± 0.007
	65.9	0.053 ± 0.007
	71.0	0.038 ± 0.007
71 mev	45.8	0.067 ± 0.009

TABLE A-3 (*Continued*)

Author, Energy	θ cm.	Polarization
Palmieri (1958)		
78 mev	45.8	0.094 ± 0.007
86 mev	45.9	0.104 ± 0.007
95 mev	20.6	0.092 ± 0.010
	25.7	0.111 ± 0.008
	30.7	0.130 ± 0.007
	35.8	0.131 ± 0.007
	40.9	0.112 ± 0.007
	46.0	0.126 ± 0.007
	51.1	0.115 ± 0.007
	56.2	0.096 ± 0.007
	61.2	0.099 ± 0.007
	66.3	0.087 ± 0.007
	71.3	0.069 ± 0.008
	76.4	0.058 ± 0.007
	81.4	0.038 ± 0.007
	86.4	0.023 ± 0.007
Palmieri (1958)		
102 mev	30.8	0.136 ± 0.008
	46.1	0.149 ± 0.007
	66.4	0.102 ± 0.007
107 mev	30.8	0.157 ± 0.009
	46.1	0.131 ± 0.007
	66.5	0.103 ± 0.007
Palmieri (1958)		
118 mev	20.6	0.112 ± 0.010
	25.8	0.146 ± 0.010
	30.9	0.152 ± 0.008
	36.0	0.173 ± 0.008
	41.1	0.170 ± 0.008
	46.2	0.149 ± 0.007
	51.4	0.169 ± 0.007
	56.5	0.134 ± 0.007
	61.5	0.126 ± 0.008
	66.6	0.110 ± 0.008
	71.7	0.108 ± 0.008

TABLE A-3 *(Continued)*

Author, Energy	θ cm.	Polarization
	76.7	0.080 ± 0.008
	81.7	0.038 ± 0.008
	86.8	0.029 ± 0.009
	91.8	0.003 ± 0.009
	96.7	-0.028 ± 0.009
127 mev	31.0	0.193 ± 0.008
	46.3	0.187 ± 0.007
	66.7	0.104 ± 0.008
137 mev	31.1	0.195 ± 0.005
	46.4	0.212 ± 0.007
	66.9	0.133 ± 0.008
Taylor (1960)		
98 mev	10.2	0.029 ± 0.031
Abs. error	12.3	-0.004 ± 0.033
1 ± 0.02	14.3	$+0.024 \pm 0.039$
	16.4	$+0.085 \pm 0.035$
	18.5	$+0.123 \pm 0.035$
	20.5	0.111 ± 0.019
	22.6	0.093 ± 0.018
	25.6	0.114 ± 0.015
	30.7	0.125 ± 0.013
	40.9	0.121 ± 0.010
	51.1	0.105 ± 0.010
	61.3	0.107 ± 0.015
	71.4	0.073 ± 0.012
	81.4	0.043 ± 0.011
Taylor (1960)		
142 mev	5.19	-0.037 ± 0.034
Abs. error	6.23	-0.027 ± 0.009
1 ± 0.02	8.30	0.031 ± 0.024
	9.34	0.089 ± 0.023
	10.38	0.122 ± 0.019
	12.46	0.130 ± 0.033
	14.53	0.180 ± 0.031
	16.61	0.155 ± 0.028
	20.76	0.190 ± 0.009
	24.80	0.216 ± 0.037

TABLE A-3   (*Continued*)

Author, Energy	θ cm.	Polarization
	25.95	0.225 ± 0.011
	31.06	0.241 ± 0.010
	37.20	0.283 ± 0.030
	41.34	0.237 ± 0.011
	45.45	0.242 ± 0.005
	49.55	0.240 ± 0.004
	51.60	0.232 ± 0.007
	53.65	0.213 ± 0.004
	57.70	0.205 ± 0.006
	59.75	0.197 ± 0.005
	61.80	0.180 ± 0.005
	65.90	0.170 ± 0.005
	69.95	0.141 ± 0.005
	72.00	0.117 ± 0.005
	74.05	0.097 ± 0.006
	78.05	0.054 ± 0.007
	82.10	0.060 ± 0.008
	90.00	0.010 ± 0.011
Palmieri (1958)		
147 ± 1 mev	6.20	-0.004 ± 0.014
Abs. error	8.34	$+0.045 \pm 0.014$
1 ± 0.03	10.4	0.103 ± 0.014
	12.4	0.126 ± 0.011
	14.5	0.155 ± 0.014
	16.6	0.180 ± 0.010
	18.7	0.193 ± 0.015
	20.7	0.198 ± 0.009
	22.8	0.183 ± 0.015
	24.9	0.227 ± 0.014
	25.9	0.203 ± 0.011
	31.1	0.228 ± 0.009
	36.3	0.247 ± 0.011
	41.4	0.239 ± 0.006
	46.5	0.233 ± 0.006
	51.7	0.229 ± 0.006
	56.8	0.205 ± 0.006
	61.9	0.171 ± 0.006

TABLE A-3   *(Continued)*

Author, Energy	θ cm.	Polarization
	67.0	0.154 ± 0.006
	72.0	0.131 ± 0.006
	77.1	0.098 ± 0.006
	82.1	0.052 ± 0.008
	87.2	0.030 ± 0.008
	92.2	-0.006 ± 0.009
	97.1	-0.041 ± 0.007
	102.1	-0.068 ± 0.008
	107.1	-0.109 ± 0.008
	112.0	-0.144 ± 0.009
Tinlot (1961)		
210 mev	$30°$	0.312 ± 0.009
Abs. error	$40°$	0.319 ± 0.011
1 ± 0.022	$50°$	0.303 ± 0.010
	$60°$	0.240 ± 0.009
	$70°$	0.163 ± 0.008
	$80°$	0.084 ± 0.007
	$90°$	-0.002 ± 0.007
Tinlot (1961)		
217 mev	$60°$	0.246 ± 0.010
Abs. error	$70°$	0.153 ± 0.009
1 ± 0.022	$80°$	0.079 ± 0.008
	$90°$	0.014 ± 0.011
	$100°$	-0.090 ± 0.009
	$110°$	-0.153 ± 0.010
	$120°$	-0.218 ± 0.011
Chamberlain (1957)		
276 mev	19.3	$+0.314 \pm 0.036$
Abs. error	27.8	$+0.324 \pm 0.041$
1 ± 0.04	32.0	$+0.329 \pm 0.028$
	49.9	$+0.295 \pm 0.027$
	63.4	$+0.251 \pm 0.027$
	76.8	$+0.122 \pm 0.021$
	90.0	$+0.044 \pm 0.019$

TABLE A-3 (*Continued*)

Author, Energy	θ cm.	Polarization
Chamberlain (1957)		
315 mev	21.6	$+0.305 \pm 0.023$
Abs. error	32.3	$+0.378 \pm 0.027$
1 ± 0.04	42.9	$+0.379 \pm 0.020$
	53.4	$+0.303 \pm 0.025$
	63.9	$+0.251 \pm 0.027$
	76.2	$+0.142 \pm 0.025$
	89.4	-0.005 ± 0.016
Kane (1954)		
415 mev	15.5	$+0.317 \pm 0.041$
Abs. error	22	$+0.353 \pm 0.027$
1 ± 0.05	33	$+0.421 \pm 0.036$
	43.5	$+0.402 \pm 0.029$
	55.5	$+0.317 \pm 0.028$
	65	$+0.260 \pm 0.030$
	75	$+0.117 \pm 0.021$
	90	-0.017 ± 0.023
Chamberlain (1957)		
310 mev	6.5	-0.21 ± 0.27
Abs. error	7.6	$+0.11 \pm 0.28$
1 ± 0.04	8.7	$+0.02 \pm 0.13$
	11.0	$+0.19 \pm 0.07$
	13.0	$+0.25 \pm 0.05$
	17.3	$+0.25 \pm 0.04$
	21.7	$+0.37 \pm 0.04$
Mesheriakov (1957)		
635 mev	11.6	-0.022 ± 0.095
Abs. error	16.2	$+0.197 \pm 0.046$
1 ± 0.05	20.8	0.276 ± 0.039
	27.6	0.395 ± 0.030
	34.4	0.400 ± 0.030
	41.2	0.424 ± 0.029
	47.9	0.378 ± 0.027
	54.5	0.357 ± 0.023
	61.0	0.307 ± 0.021
	67.5	0.279 ± 0.027
	73.8	0.195 ± 0.028

TABLE A-3   (*Continued*)

Author, Energy	θ cm.	Polarization
	80.1	0.167 ± 0.026
	86.3	0.084 ± 0.040
	90.3	-0.016 ± 0.025
Homer (1962)		
970 mev	12.3	0.24 ± 0.15
1 ± 0.15	22.1	0.18 ± 0.08
	24.5	0.22 ± 0.05
	26.9	0.31 ± 0.05
	29.4	0.24 ± 0.08
	30.5	0.23 ± 0.05
	36.5	0.30 ± 0.05
	48.3	0.39 ± 0.04
	59.7	0.33 ± 0.07
	70.8	0.17 ± 0.06
	81.6	0.06 ± 0.07
Bareyre (1961)		
1.7 Bev	9	0.15 ± 0.04
Abs. error	15	0.11 ± 0.05
1 ± 0.21	21	0.10 ± 0.05
	28	0.20 ± 0.06
	40	0.30 ± 0.08
	45	0.25 ± 0.03
	54	0.30 ± 0.06
	68	0.02 ± 0.08
	108	-0.08 ± 0.2

TABLE A-4   *pp* TRIPLE SCATTERING PARAMETERS

Author, Energy	θ cm.	Value
Griffith (1963)		
50 mev	70	-0.249 ± 0.075
D		
Thorndike (1960)		
98 mev	21	0.00 ± 0.08
D	31	0.00 ± 0.07
	41	0.00 ± 0.08
	51	-0.12 ± 0.10
	61	-0.11 ± 0.16
Hwang (1960)		
142 mev	12.4	-0.262 ± 0.063
D	20.7	-0.008 ± 0.038
	31.1	$+0.137 \pm 0.033$
	41.4	0.156 ± 0.031
	51.7	0.178 ± 0.033
	61.9	0.076 ± 0.031
	72.0	0.147 ± 0.070
	82.1	0.286 ± 0.099
Thorndike (1961)		
140 mev	31.1	-0.252 ± 0.030
R	41.4	-0.227 ± 0.028
	51.7	-0.271 ± 0.035
	61.9	-0.146 ± 0.037
	72.0	-0.151 ± 0.055
	82.1	-0.047 ± 0.080
Bird (1963)		
141 mev	24.0	-0.224 ± 0.051
R	32.7	-0.203 ± 0.051
	45.7	-0.178 ± 0.031
	54.4	-0.212 ± 0.042
	67.2	-0.213 ± 0.040
	76.1	-0.147 ± 0.063
	84.0	-0.142 ± 0.136
	90.0	$+0.110 \pm 0.131$
Hee (1962)		
139 mev	31.1	-0.368 ± 0.032
A	41.4	-0.344 ± 0.031
	51.7	-0.311 ± 0.035
	61.9	-0.231 ± 0.046
	72.0	-0.189 ± 0.056
	82.1	-0.099 ± 0.079

TABLE A-4   (*Continued*)

Author, Energy	θ cm.	Value
Bird (1961)		
143 mev	31	$+0.082 \pm 0.077$
D	41	$+0.162 \pm 0.040$
	51.5	$+0.110 \pm 0.050$
	62	$+0.045 \pm 0.060$
	72	$+0.019 \pm 0.100$
	82	-0.037 ± 0.133
	92	-0.027 ± 0.170
Jarvis (1963)		
143 mev	32.2	-0.405 ± 0.032
A	43.2	-0.377 ± 0.037
	54.6	-0.342 ± 0.050
	65.0	-0.355 ± 0.075
	74.8	-0.198 ± 0.079
	84.8	$+0.022 \pm 0.154$
Hee (1962)		
137.5 mev	43	0.562 ± 0.052
R'	52.5	0.472 ± 0.054
	62	0.376 ± 0.068
	72.5	0.238 ± 0.084
	82.1	0.251 ± 0.121
England (1961)		
213 mev	$30°$	-0.203 ± 0.012
R	$40°$	-0.133 ± 0.017
	$50°$	-0.041 ± 0.018
	$60°$	$+0.071 \pm 0.026$
	$70°$	$+0.147 \pm 0.029$
	$80°$	$+0.248 \pm 0.042$
	$90°$	$+0.223 \pm 0.055$
England (1961)		
213 mev	$30°$	-0.400 ± 0.019
A	$40°$	-0.317 ± 0.019
	$50°$	-0.205 ± 0.021
	$60°$	-0.102 ± 0.025
	$70°$	-0.012 ± 0.036
	$80°$	-0.090 ± 0.046
	$90°$	-0.180 ± 0.077
Heer (1962)		
213 mev	$30°$	0.200 ± 0.016
D	$40°$	0.232 ± 0.026
	$50°$	0.240 ± 0.018

TABLE A-4 *(Continued)*

Author, Energy	θ cm.	Value
	60°	0.319 ± 0.021
	70°	0.297 ± 0.030
	80°	0.36 ± 0.07
	90°	0.50 ± 0.18
Lobkowicz (1962) 213 mev R'	30°	0.538 ± 0.028
	40°	0.390 ± 0.028
	50°	0.193 ± 0.026
	60°	−0.055 ± 0.066
Chamberlain (1957) 310 mev D	23.1	0.245 ± 0.079
	25.8	0.299 ± 0.055
	36.5	0.456 ± 0.081
	52.0	0.533 ± 0.060
	65.0	0.503 ± 0.048
	80.5	0.472 ± 0.063
Chamberlain (1957) 310 mev R	22.4	−0.324 ± 0.139
	34.4	−0.167 ± 0.080
	41.8	+0.104 ± 0.071
	54.1	0.287 ± 0.052
	70.9	0.310 ± 0.072
	80.1	0.576 ± 0.087
Simmons (1956) 316 mev A	25.4	−0.339 ± 0.064
	51.4	+0.007 ± 0.045
	76.3	0.236 ± 0.050
Kumekin (1958) 660 mev D	54°	0.99 ± 0.25
	72°	0.69 ± 0.20
	90°	0.93 ± 0.17
	108°	0.28 ± 0.16
	126°	0.57 ± 0.20
Kumekin (1962) 640 mev R	54°	0.45 ± 0.08
	72°	0.49 ± 0.08
	90°	0.23 ± 0.07
	108°	0.32 ± 0.06
	126°	0.49 ± 0.13

TABLE A-5 np TOTAL CROSS SECTIONS
(See also Tables 2-6 and 6-1)

Author	σ_{tot}(mb)	E(mev)
Poss (1952)	689 ± 5	14.10 ± 0.05
Day (1955)	495 ± 3	19.66 ± 0.04
Taylor (1952)	223 ± 8	38 ± 1
	126 ± 3	63 ± 1
	74 ± 3	95 ± 2
	57 ± 2	126 ± 2
	46.4 ± 1.2	153 ± 3
Hillman (1954)	196 ± 16	45 ± 1
	86 ± 2	88 ± 2
	84 ± 2	88 ± 2
Mott (1952)	44 ± 12	180 ± 7
	41.3 ± 3.5	220 ± 10
Kazarinov (1962)	42.5 ± 0.9	200
Ashmore (1957)	35.6 ± 0.7	350
Nedzel (1954)	33.7 ± 1.3	410
Dzelepov (1955)	35 ± 2	500
	36 ± 2	590
	37 ± 4	630
Coor (1955)	42.4 ± 1.8	1400
Bowen (1961)	537 ± 30	15.80 ± 0.33
Systematic errors	634 ± 34	16.13 ± 0.33
of ± 2% in E	580 ± 33	16.46 ± 0.34
and ± 2% in σ	597 ± 32	16.80 ± 0.35
	561 ± 29	17.15 ± 0.36
	544 ± 28	17.52 ± 0.37
	533 ± 27	17.90 ± 0.39
	517 ± 27	18.29 ± 0.40
	523 ± 28	18.69 ± 0.42
	498 ± 40	19.11 ± 0.43
	522 ± 26	19.55 ± 0.44
	479 ± 24	20.00 ± 0.46
	479 ± 22	20.46 ± 0.47
	449 ± 21	20.93 ± 0.48
	447 ± 20	21.41 ± 0.50
	420 ± 20	21.91 ± 0.51
	408 ± 20	22.43 ± 0.52
	433 ± 19	22.96 ± 0.54
	397.7 ± 16	23.51 ± 0.57
	393.0 ± 15	24.09 ± 0.59
	393.5 ± 14	24.69 ± 0.61
	362.9 ± 13.5	25.31 ± 0.63
	377.6 ± 12.7	25.94 ± 0.65
	345.7 ± 12.3	26.60 ± 0.68

TABLE A-5   (*Continued*)

Author	σ_{tot}(mb)	E(mev)
	335.4 ± 11.5	27.29 ± 0.72
	321.5 ± 11.0	28.03 ± 0.76
	312.2 ± 10.5	28.80 ± 0.78
	309.1 ± 9.5	29.59 ± 0.80
	281.7 ± 8.8	30.40 ± 0.83
	286.4 ± 8.3	31.24 ± 0.86
	288.7 ± 7.4	32.12 ± 0.90
	276.0 ± 6.8	33.05 ± 0.96
	260.1 ± 7.2	34.03 ± 1.01
	245.8 ± 6.7	35.08 ± 1.07
	220.0 ± 9.9	36.20 ± 1.12
	226.8 ± 6.3	37.32 ± 1.15
	223.5 ± 6.0	38.48 ± 1.21
	219.1 ± 5.7	39.75 ± 1.29
	204.6 ± 5.4	41.10 ± 1.38
	196.0 ± 5.2	42.53 ± 1.45
	189.1 ± 4.9	44.00 ± 1.50
	187.3 ± 4.6	45.50 ± 1.60
	170.3 ± 4.0	47.10 ± 1.70
	166.8 ± 4.1	48.80 ± 1.80
	152.0 ± 3.8	50.60 ± 1.90
	152.0 ± 3.6	52.5 ± 2.0
	144.8 ± 3.3	54.5 ± 2.1
	141.5 ± 3.1	56.6 ± 2.2
	135.8 ± 2.9	58.8 ± 2.3
	124.3 ± 2.8	61.1 ± 2.4
	116.8 ± 2.6	63.5 ± 2.5
	114.9 ± 2.5	66.1 ± 2.7
	109.6 ± 2.3	68.9 ± 3.0
	100.1 ± 2.3	72.0 ± 3.2
	100.3 ± 3.6	75.3 ± 3.5
	94.7 ± 2.1	78.9 ± 3.8
	85.3 ± 1.9	82.8 ± 4.0
	82.1 ± 1.9	86.9 ± 4.3
	77.7 ± 1.7	91.3 ± 4.6
	72.1 ± 1.6	96.0 ± 4.8
	71.5 ± 1.7	101.0 ± 5.0
	69.4 ± 1.6	106.0 ± 5.3
	68.3 ± 2.1	111.5 ± 5.7
Chen (1956) $pd - pp$ Values, therefore low	31.0 ± 1.4	380
	31.5 ± 1.8	590
	28.4 ± 1.2	810
	27.0 ± 2.0	1060
	32.1 ± 1.3	1260
	33.6 ± 1.9	1480
	34.3 ± 2.0	2000
	31.4 ± 1.8	2600

TABLE A-6 *np* DIFFERENTIAL CROSS SECTIONS

Author, Energy	θ cm.	$d\sigma/d\Omega$ cm. mb/ster. ($\pm\%$)
Flynn (1962)	175	35.9 ± 12
22.5 mev	165	34.3 ± 7.5
Relative only	155	34.0 ± 5.7
	145	37.0 ± 4.7
	135	35.6 ± 4.3
	125	34.7 ± 4.0
	115	32.4 ± 4.0
	105	32.2 ± 3.8
	95	33.2 ± 3.7
	85	32.7 ± 3.7
	75	32.8 ± 4.5
	65	33.3 ± 5.7
Bowen (1962)	7	28.5 ± 3.7
27.5 mev	14	28.5 ± 4.7
Only counting	21	29.6 ± 5.2
errors are here	31	28.3 ± 3.5
quoted (in %)	41	27.5 ± 4.3
Systematic and	51	27.3 ± 3.2
normalization	62	26.5 ± 4.6
errors are	72	27.0 ± 3.6
about 3% (see	159	25.3 ± 3.2
reference)	166	26.8 ± 2.8
	173	29.9 ± 3.1
Bowen (1962)	7	32.8 ± 3.6
22.6 mev	14	32.6 ± 4.7
	21	35.6 ± 5.1
	31	34.4 ± 3.3
	41	32.8 ± 4.1
	51	35.5 ± 3.0
Bowen (1962)	7	25.7 ± 3.7
32.5 mev	14	25.9 ± 4.6
	21	27.1 ± 5.1
	31	26.9 ± 3.3
	41	24.4 ± 4.2

TABLE A-6   (Continued)

Author, Energy	θ cm.	$d\sigma/d\Omega$ cm. mb/ster. ($\pm\%$)
	51	24.3 ± 3.1
	62	24.2 ± 4.6
	72	21.3 ± 3.8
	82	22.1 ± 5.3
	129	19.6 ± 3.5
	139	21.5 ± 3.1
	149	24.0 ± 3.4
	159	23.8 ± 3.5
	166	25.8 ± 3.1
	173	25.6 ± 3.6
Bowen (1962)	7	21.9 ± 3.7
37.5 mev	14	21.9 ± 4.8
	21	21.6 ± 5.2
	31	20.7 ± 3.3
	41	19.7 ± 4.1
	51	21.4 ± 3.0
	62	18.7 ± 4.6
	72	18.7 ± 3.7
	82	16.8 ± 5.3
	92	16.5 ± 4.1
	118	16.3 ± 3.7
	129	18.7 ± 3.4
	139	17.9 ± 3.4
	149	19.6 ± 3.7
	159	19.3 ± 4.2
	166	22.0 ± 3.5
	173	21.4 ± 4.1
Bowen (1962)	7	19.9 ± 4.0
42.5 mev	14	20.8 ± 4.6
	21	20.2 ± 5.1
	31	18.6 ± 3.2
	41	15.8 ± 4.1
	51	17.1 ± 3.0
	62	18.3 ± 4.6
	72	14.0 ± 3.8

TABLE A-6 *(Continued)*

Author, Energy	θ cm.	$d\sigma/d\Omega$ cm. mb/ster. ($\pm\%$)
	82	14.1 ± 5.5
	92	14.0 ± 4.2
	102	13.4 ± 6.6
	78	12.1 ± 9.6
	88	12.4 ± 7.7
	98	16.8 ± 5.7
	108	14.9 ± 3.0
	118	15.5 ± 3.0
	129	15.8 ± 2.8
	139	15.9 ± 3.8
	149	16.5 ± 4.2
	159	18.7 ± 4.1
	166	18.7 ± 3.9
	173	18.7 ± 4.6
Bowen (1962)	7	19.10 ± 3.8
47.5 mev	14	18.80 ± 4.6
	21	19.20 ± 5.1
	31	16.82 ± 3.5
	41	15.77 ± 4.4
	51	14.79 ± 3.3
	62	12.78 ± 4.9
	72	13.09 ± 4.0
	82	12.83 ± 5.7
	92	12.25 ± 4.4
	102	10.32 ± 6.1
	78	12.63 ± 8.8
	88	12.55 ± 8.4
	98	13.68 ± 6.9
	108	12.79 ± 3.6
	118	14.32 ± 2.9
	129	14.40 ± 3.2
	139	13.50 ± 3.9
	149	15.11 ± 4.5
	159	16.22 ± 4.6
	166	16.88 ± 4.1
	173	17.68 ± 4.9

TABLE A-6 *(Continued)*

Author, Energy	θ cm.	$d\sigma/d\Omega$ cm. mb/ster. ($\pm\%$)
Bowen (1962) 52.5 mev	7	18.36 ± 3.8
	14	18.02 ± 4.5
	21	18.18 ± 5.1
	31	14.89 ± 3.6
	41	14.16 ± 4.6
	51	12.91 ± 3.4
	62	12.36 ± 5.0
	72	10.98 ± 3.9
	82	10.88 ± 6.1
	92	10.36 ± 4.5
	102	9.50 ± 7.5
	112	11.12 ± 7.9
	78	11.60 ± 10.1
	88	12.61 ± 8.5
	98	11.38 ± 8.4
	108	11.64 ± 3.8
	118	12.20 ± 3.4
	129	12.04 ± 4.0
	139	12.91 ± 4.0
	149	14.83 ± 4.9
	159	14.99 ± 5.2
	166	17.80 ± 4.3
	173	17.01 ± 5.3
Bowen (1962) 57.5 mev	7	17.36 ± 4.0
	14	15.52 ± 5.0
	21	16.61 ± 5.3
	31	13.76 ± 3.8
	41	13.06 ± 5.0
	51	11.37 ± 3.6
	62	10.73 ± 5.3
	72	9.43 ± 4.1
	82	9.09 ± 6.1
	92	9.75 ± 4.5
	102	9.18 ± 7.6
	112	9.17 ± 9.3

TABLE A-6   (*Continued*)

Author, Energy	θ cm.	$d\sigma/d\Omega$ cm. mb/ster. $(\pm\%)$
	78	6.65 ± 17.0
	88	9.89 ± 10.3
	98	11.06 ± 8.3
	108	10.31 ± 4.0
	118	9.73 ± 3.8
	129	10.56 ± 4.1
	139	12.58 ± 4.0
	149	12.87 ± 5.4
	159	14.49 ± 5.2
	166	16.10 ± 4.5
	173	14.80 ± 5.5
Bowen (1962)	7	15.39 ± 4.5
62.5 mev	14	15.36 ± 5.5
	21	14.96 ± 6.0
	31	13.18 ± 3.9
	41	11.72 ± 5.1
	51	9.55 ± 3.7
	62	8.98 ± 6.1
	72	7.43 ± 4.8
	82	6.23 ± 7.1
	92	7.43 ± 5.2
	102	8.38 ± 7.8
	112	9.02 ± 8.0
	78	7.85 ± 12.7
	88	7.72 ± 12.5
	98	9.90 ± 8.5
	108	8.84 ± 4.9
	118	8.69 ± 4.1
	129	9.08 ± 4.1
	139	10.56 ± 4.3
	149	11.76 ± 5.7
	159	12.74 ± 5.2
	166	13.00 ± 4.8
	173	13.70 ± 5.9

TABLE A-6   (*Continued*)

Author, Energy	θ cm.	$d\sigma/d\Omega$ cm. mb/ster. ($\pm\%$)
Bowen (1962)	7	13.93 ± 3.5
70 mev	14	14.02 ± 4.7
	21	12.45 ± 5.1
	31	12.75 ± 3.5
	41	10.43 ± 4.7
	51	8.55 ± 3.3
	62	7.66 ± 5.1
	72	6.59 ± 3.9
	82	6.76 ± 5.2
	92	6.19 ± 3.7
	102	6.38 ± 6.3
	112	5.70 ± 7.1
	122	6.70 ± 7.9
	78	5.41 ± 13.4
	88	6.00 ± 10.7
	98	5.48 ± 10.3
	108	6.46 ± 4.1
	118	7.58 ± 3.1
	129	8.02 ± 3.1
	139	8.62 ± 3.4
	149	10.79 ± 4.3
	159	12.75 ± 3.8
	166	12.52 ± 3.6
	173	13.24 ± 4.4
Bowen (1962)	7	11.26 ± 3.9
80 mev	14	11.34 ± 4.9
	21	10.77 ± 5.3
	31	9.50 ± 3.7
	41	8.23 ± 4.9
	51	8.08 ± 3.4
	62	7.05 ± 5.6
	72	5.90 ± 4.4
	82	5.10 ± 5.9
	92	5.53 ± 4.4
	102	5.27 ± 6.7
	112	6.67 ± 7.5

TABLE A-6   (*Continued*)

Author, Energy	θ cm.	$d\sigma/d\Omega$ cm. mb/ster. ($\pm\%$)
	122	4.86 ± 10.9
	78	6.09 ± 12.2
	88	5.62 ± 11.5
	98	4.09 ± 13.7
	108	6.13 ± 4.4
	118	6.64 ± 3.5
	129	7.62 ± 3.5
	139	8.48 ± 3.5
	149	9.80 ± 4.9
	159	10.93 ± 4.8
	166	12.05 ± 4.0
	173	12.80 ± 4.7
Bowen (1962)	7	11.86 ± 4.1
89.5 mev	14	9.80 ± 5.1
	21	9.32 ± 5.9
	31	8.52 ± 4.2
	41	7.24 ± 5.7
	51	6.00 ± 4.0
	62	5.60 ± 6.1
	72	5.05 ± 4.9
	82	4.35 ± 6.6
	92	4.49 ± 4.9
	102	4.79 ± 7.6
	112	4.55 ± 8.9
	122	6.23 ± 8.7
	78	4.96 ± 14.8
	88	3.41 ± 17.9
	98	4.30 ± 13.1
	108	5.60 ± 4.7
	118	5.42 ± 4.4
	129	6.52 ± 4.0
	139	8.03 ± 3.7
	149	8.27 ± 5.4
	159	10.33 ± 4.8
	166	11.84 ± 4.4
	173	12.47 ± 4.7

TABLE A-6 *(Continued)*

Author, Energy	θ cm.	$d\sigma/d\Omega$ cm. mb/ster. $(\pm\%)$
Bowen (1962) 99 mev	7	10.97 ± 4.4
	14	9.68 ± 5.3
	21	7.81 ± 6.1
	31	8.41 ± 5.1
	41	6.30 ± 6.1
	51	5.08 ± 4.4
	62	4.45 ± 7.1
	72	4.14 ± 6.1
	82	3.56 ± 8.3
	92	3.60 ± 5.9
	102	4.37 ± 9.2
	112	3.86 ± 10.3
	122	4.80 ± 12.2
	78	2.09 ± 36.4
	88	2.83 ± 22.2
	98	4.10 ± 13.2
	108	4.93 ± 5.0
	118	5.70 ± 3.9
	129	6.57 ± 4.5
	139	7.33 ± 4.2
	149	9.26 ± 5.8
	159	9.51 ± 4.9
	166	11.53 ± 4.7
	173	12.31 ± 5.2
Bowen (1962) 108.5 mev	7	11.10 ± 5.1
	14	8.22 ± 7.3
	21	7.83 ± 7.3
	31	7.38 ± 5.1
	41	5.26 ± 7.6
	51	4.71 ± 5.4
	62	4.09 ± 8.6
	72	3.69 ± 6.8
	82	3.50 ± 8.6
	92	3.70 ± 6.1
	102	3.48 ± 9.4

TABLE A-6   (*Continued*)

Author, Energy	θ cm.	$d\sigma/d\Omega$ cm. mb/ster. ($\pm\%$)
	112	5.10 ± 10.2
	122	5.61 ± 9.8
	78	1.92 ± 39.0
	88	2.87 ± 22.4
	98	3.26 ± 18.2
	108	5.03 ± 5.8
	118	4.44 ± 5.7
	129	6.35 ± 4.9
	139	8.13 ± 4.3
	149	8.77 ± 5.8
	159	9.47 ± 4.9
	166	11.01 ± 5.0
	173	12.12 ± 5.5
Stahl (1954)	176.6	13.08 ± 0.41
91 mev	175.6	13.09 ± 0.38
Relative only	173.7	13.30 ± 0.33
Error in mb/ster.,	171.7	13.24 ± 0.35
not in %	169.7	12.61 ± 0.32
	167.3	11.84 ± 0.30
	164.5	11.82 ± 0.31
	162.0	10.85 ± 0.33
	159.4	10.42 ± 0.29
	159.4	10.84 ± 0.43
	154.9	9.97 ± 0.30
	149.3	9.13 ± 0.24
	139.1	7.74 ± 0.19
	139.1	8.08 ± 0.28
	129.0	6.51 ± 0.17
	118.8	5.99 ± 0.15
	108.7	4.93 ± 0.16
	98.7	4.53 ± 0.14
	88.7	4.19 ± 0.15
	82.7	3.97 ± 0.13
	78.7	4.17 ± 0.15
	74.7	4.08 ± 0.19

TABLE A-6   (*Continued*)

Author, Energy	θ cm.	$d\sigma/d\Omega$ cm. mb/ster.
	69.7	4.26 ± 0.18
	64.8	4.88 ± 0.29
	59.8	5.61 ± 0.33
Hobbie (1960)	169.7	11.37 ± 0.41
128 mev	159.3	9.08 ± 0.33
Relative only	149.0	7.30 ± 0.26
	138.8	6.28 ± 0.23
	128.5	5.20 ± 0.19
	118.4	4.29 ± 0.15
	108.2	3.45 ± 0.12
	98.1	2.83 ± 0.11
	88.1	2.61 ± 0.09
	78.1	2.74 ± 0.11
Voss (1955)	6.3	9.06 ± 1.0
137 ± 3 mev	10.6	8.16 ± 0.6
Abs. error	20.7	7.02 ± 0.4
1 ± 0.05	31.0	5.96 ± 0.35
	41.3	4.46 ± 0.4
	51.6	2.91 ± 0.4
	61.8	2.75 ± 0.4
Randle (1956)	20–30	6.55 ± 0.75
133 mev	30–40	5.59 ± 0.59
Relative only	40–50	3.86 ± 0.44
	50–60	3.31 ± 0.38
	60–70	2.45 ± 0.31
	70–80	2.96 ± 0.33
	80–90	2.64 ± 0.31
	90–100	2.54 ± 0.30
	100–110	3.13 ± 0.34
	110–120	3.80 ± 0.39
	120–130	5.31 ± 0.48
	130–140	5.23 ± 0.51
	140–150	6.13 ± 0.62
	150–160	8.75 ± 0.87

TABLE A-6 (*Continued*)

Author, Energy	θ cm.	$d\sigma/d\Omega$ cm. mb/ster.
Randle (1952)	50	2.96 ± 0.43
153 ± 3 mev	56	2.14 ± 0.40
Relative only	65.5	2.59 ± 0.40
	68	2.34 ± 0.18
	76.5	1.98 ± 0.22
	83	1.98 ± 0.19
	89.5	2.29 ± 0.18
	98	2.71 ± 0.31
	99.5	2.51 ± 0.19
	112	3.87 ± 0.18
	124.5	4.04 ± 0.28
	138	6.19 ± 0.26
	149	6.88 ± 0.43
	159	7.98 ± 0.13
	165	8.59 ± 0.29
	171	10.04 ± 0.20
	174	9.68 ± 0.47
	176	10.65 ± 0.46
	178	10.69 ± 0.54
Kazarinov (1960)	6.25	9.5 ± 2.5
200 mev	10.5	8.3 ± 0.8
Relative only	21.3	4.7 ± 0.7
	31.5	4.1 ± 0.5
	41.7	3.0 ± 0.4
	62.7	2.4 ± 0.4
	67.3	2.16 ± 0.16
	77.3	1.91 ± 0.07
	87	1.87 ± 0.08
	97	2.20 ± 0.08
	109.3	2.79 ± 0.16
	117.5	3.51 ± 0.24
	129.6	3.85 ± 0.16
	139.3	4.63 ± 0.16
	148.5	5.79 ± 0.12
	159	7.02 ± 0.13
	163	7.78 ± 0.24
	165	9.22 ± 0.26

TABLE A-6   (*Continued*)

Author, Energy	θ cm.	$d\sigma/d\Omega$ cm. mb/ster.
	169.5	10.33 ± 0.23
	173.75	11.29 ± 0.24
	180	11.4 ± 0.4
Kelly (1950)	37.7	3.6 ± 0.7
260 mev	47.2	3.3 ± 0.6
Relative only	56.8	1.1 ± 0.6
	66.6	1.7 ± 0.4
	76.4	1.9 ± 0.7
	86.3	1.85 ± 0.14
	96.3	1.09 ± 0.26
	106.5	2.02 ± 0.21
	116.7	1.90 ± 0.24
	127.1	2.8 ± 0.4
	137.6	4.5 ± 0.3
	148.1	4.7 ± 0.4
	158.7	6.4 ± 0.3
	169.3	7.8 ± 0.8
	180	13.7 ± 2.1
De Pangher (1955)	30–40	3.81 ± 0.41
300 mev	40–50	3.50 ± 0.35
Relative only	50–60	2.96 ± 0.28
	60–70	2.31 ± 0.31
	70–80	2.02 ± 0.20
	80–90	1.89 ± 0.18
	90–100	1.51 ± 0.14
	100–110	2.07 ± 0.16
	110–120	2.17 ± 0.17
	120–130	2.51 ± 0.19
	130–140	3.06 ± 0.23
	140–150	4.06 ± 0.29
	150–160	4.71 ± 0.37
	160–170	6.48 ± 0.55
	170–180	9.14 ± 1.12
Easley (1954)	10.7	5.6 ± 1.1
290 mev	21.7	4.3 ± 0.9
Relative only	37.8	3.6 ± 0.7

TABLE A-6 (*Continued*)

Author, Energy	θ cm.	$d\sigma/d\Omega$ cm. mb/ster.
Ashmore (1962)	173°45′	10.50 ± 0.14
350 mev	173°34′	10.19 ± 0.14
Relative only	170°31′	8.83 ± 0.12
	167°11′	7.44 ± 0.10
	165°5′	6.95 ± 0.10
	162°54′	6.42 ± 0.09
	160°40′	6.02 ± 0.09
	165°5′	7.00 ± 0.08
	162°54′	6.35 ± 0.08
	160°40′	5.95 ± 0.07
	156°20′	5.38 ± 0.07
	152°8′	5.02 ± 0.06
	147°52′	4.546 ± 0.059
	142°19′	4.000 ± 0.052
	137°7′	3.504 ± 0.045
	125°29′	2.565 ± 0.034
	114°9′	1.942 ± 0.028
Hartzler (1954)	12.7	3.73 ± 2.10
400 mev	15	4.43 ± 0.46
Relative only	20	3.07 ± 0.37
	30	2.84 ± 0.57
	40	3.33 ± 0.20
	45	3.35 ± 0.20
	50	3.38 ± 0.12
	55	2.56 ± 0.23
	60	2.48 ± 0.08
	70	2.22 ± 0.09
	80	1.85 ± 0.06
	90	1.54 ± 0.06
	100	1.42 ± 0.08
	110	1.50 ± 0.08
	120	1.94 ± 0.08
	130	2.50 ± 0.09
	140	3.21 ± 0.09
	150	4.17 ± 0.11
	160	5.25 ± 0.14

TABLE A-6   (*Continued*)

Author, Energy	θ cm.	$d\sigma/d\Omega$ cm. mb/ster.
	165	5.82 ± 0.22
	170	7.93 ± 0.28
	175	9.57 ± 0.34
	180	13.49 ± 0.91
Kazarinov (1956)	35	3.7 ± 0.20
580 mev	45	3.0 ± 0.30
Relative only	54	2.3 ± 0.20
	63	2.1 ± 0.20
	73	1.6 ± 0.10
	83	1.1 ± 0.10
	93	0.91 ± 0.06
	103	0.78 ± 0.05
	114	0.78 ± 0.05
	124	1.0 ± 0.07
	135	1.7 ± 0.10
	147	2.1 ± 0.20
	157	3.4 ± 0.30
	169	5.3 ± 0.50
	180	8.5 ± 0.80
Golovin (1958)	5	10 ± 2
Amoglobeli (1958)	8	8.2 ± 1.4
590 mev	11.5	6.4 ± 0.9
Relative only	23	4.3 ± 0.5
	35	3.7 ± 0.2
Amoglobeli (1959)	11	8.2 ± 1.0
630 mev	25	5.0 ± 0.7
Relative only	35	3.8 ± 0.2
Read from graph	43	2.5 ± 0.2
	52	2.15 ± 0.2
	61	1.65 ± 0.15
	71	1.50 ± 0.05
	81	1.15 ± 0.05
	91	1.00 ± 0.05

TABLE A-6   *(Continued)*

Author, Energy	θ cm.	$d\sigma/d\Omega$ cm. mb/ster.
	101	0.90 ± 0.05
	111	0.90 ± 0.05
	121	1.30 ± 0.10
	134	1.60 ± 0.1
	145	2.4 ± 0.15
	156	3.3 ± 0.3
	160	4.0 ± 0.4
	165	4.6 ± 0.4
	170	5.8 ± 0.4
	173	6.5 ± 0.4
	178	8.0 ± 0.5
Larsen (1962)	180.00	6.14 ± 0.54
710 ± 8 mev	175.89	5.04 ± 0.51
Relative only	172.94	4.39 ± 0.39
	170.60	3.97 ± 0.38
	168.25	3.84 ± 0.31
	165.90	3.12 ± 0.25
	163.25	3.35 ± 0.28
	161.37	2.71 ± 0.24
	158.90	2.65 ± 0.23
Martelli (1961)		
775 mev	90	0.89 ± 0.05
1010 mev	90	0.61 ± 0.03
Palevsky (1962)		
2040 mev	0	25 ± 1
Abs. error	1.25	22 ± 1.7
1 ± 0.25	2.5	12.5 ± 2.5
Proton lab.	3.75	9 ± 1
angles and	5.0	63 ± 1.2
cross sections.	7.5	5 ± 0.5
2850 mev	0	28.5 ± 1
Abs. error	1.25	22.5 ± 2.2
1 ± 0.25	2.5	13.0 ± 1.4
	5.0	6.8 ± 1.2

TABLE A-7 np POLARIZATION MEASUREMENTS

Author, Energy	θ cm.	Polarization
Benenson (1962)		
16.4 mev	100	0.011 ± 0.021
	120	0.052 ± 0.027
	140	0.023 ± 0.023
Perkins (1963)	50	0.049 ± 0.014
23.1 mev	70	0.053 ± 0.010
	90	0.052 ± 0.007
	110	0.031 ± 0.007
	130	0.025 ± 0.009
	150	-0.004 ± 0.009
Benenson (1962)		
23.7 mev	80	0.034 ± 0.025
	100	0.028 ± 0.021
	120	0.028 ± 0.019
	140	0.007 ± 0.021
Bowen (1961)		
20 mev	20	0.075 ± 0.053
Abs. error	30	$+0.014 \pm 0.045$
1 ± 0.17	40	$+0.093 \pm 0.045$
	50	$+0.051 \pm 0.036$
	60	$+0.076 \pm 0.045$
	70	-0.048 ± 0.045
Bowen (1961)		
30 mev	30	0.041 ± 0.032
Abs. error	40	0.132 ± 0.031
1 ± 0.083	120	0.108 ± 0.032
	140	0.023 ± 0.020
Bowen (1961)		
40 mev	20	0.069 ± 0.039
Abs. error	30	0.174 ± 0.034
1 ± 0.06	40	0.152 ± 0.031
	50	0.119 ± 0.032
	60	0.143 ± 0.038
	70	0.171 ± 0.042
	120	0.097 ± 0.020
	140	0.030 ± 0.017
Bowen (1961)		
50 mev	20	0.106 ± 0.032
Abs. error	30	0.142 ± 0.028
1 ± 0.05	40	0.167 ± 0.026
	50	0.213 ± 0.029
	60	0.244 ± 0.035
	70	0.201 ± 0.035
	120	0.097 ± 0.020
	140	0.030 ± 0.017
Bowen (1961)		
60 mev	20	0.079 ± 0.026
Abs. error	30	0.112 ± 0.024
1 ± 0.04	40	0.231 ± 0.024

TABLE A-7 (*Continued*)

Author, Energy	θ cm.	Polarization
	50	0.226 ± 0.025
	60	0.229 ± 0.029
	70	0.274 ± 0.034
	120	0.104 ± 0.013
	140	0.024 ± 0.012
Bowen (1961)		
70 mev	20	0.144 ± 0.029
Abs. error	30	0.203 ± 0.033
1 ± 0.04	40	0.292 ± 0.032
	50	0.291 ± 0.034
	60	0.266 ± 0.042
	70	0.313 ± 0.058
	120	0.094 ± 0.015
	140	0.018 ± 0.013
Bowen (1961)		
80 mev	20	0.140 ± 0.033
Abs. error	30	0.203 ± 0.033
1 ± 0.04	40	0.292 ± 0.032
	50	0.291 ± 0.034
	60	0.266 ± 0.042
	70	0.313 ± 0.058
	120	0.087 ± 0.017
	140	0.006 ± 0.016
Bowen (1961)		
90 mev	20	0.153 ± 0.040
Abs. error	30	0.298 ± 0.047
1 ± 0.05	40	0.299 ± 0.043
	50	0.344 ± 0.047
	70	0.544 ± 0.123
	120	0.107 ± 0.025
	140	-0.002 ± 0.022
Bowen (1961)		
100 mev	20	0.173 ± 0.065
Abs. error	30	0.303 ± 0.070
1 ± 0.07	40	0.438 ± 0.072
	50	0.452 ± 0.086
	120	0.008 ± 0.040
	140	-0.034 ± 0.035
Bowen (1961)		
110 mev	30	0.498 ± 0.107
Abs. error	40	0.329 ± 0.089
1 ± 0.10	120	0.036 ± 0.055
	140	-0.048 ± 0.047
Whitehead (1960)		
77 mev	20.6	0.185 ± 0.025
Abs. error	30.4	0.275 ± 0.025
1 ± 0.08	40.6	0.335 ± 0.025
	50.4	0.430 ± 0.030

TABLE A-7 *(Continued)*

Author, Energy	θ cm.	Polarization
	61.4	0.425 ± 0.020
	71.4	0.390 ± 0.025
	80.8	0.280 ± 0.030
	90.6	0.245 ± 0.025
	78.8	0.303 ± 0.012
	88.8	0.250 ± 0.009
	98.8	0.197 ± 0.009
	108.6	0.134 ± 0.009
	118.6	0.073 ± 0.008
	128.4	0.042 ± 0.008
	138.2	-0.008 ± 0.007
	149.4	-0.003 ± 0.009
	159.2	-0.009 ± 0.009
Stafford (1957)		
95 mev	22.5	0.143 ± 0.032
Abs. error	29.8	0.170 ± 0.037
1 ± 0.08	41.0	0.320 ± 0.060
	52.5	0.405 ± 0.041
	61.5	0.560 ± 0.064
	76.0	0.307 ± 0.040
	78.5	0.386 ± 0.034
	88.5	0.291 ± 0.032
	98.5	0.256 ± 0.048
	108.0	0.070 ± 0.047
	118.5	0.049 ± 0.055
	128.5	-0.055 ± 0.035
	138.5	-0.016 ± 0.028
	149.0	-0.073 ± 0.025
	159.5	-0.037 ± 0.024
Hobbie (1960)		
128 mev	169.7	$+0.002 \pm 0.021$
Abs. error	159.3	-0.045 ± 0.021
1 ± 0.08	149.0	-0.061 ± 0.021
	138.8	-0.072 ± 0.017
	128.5	-0.016 ± 0.021
	118.4	$+0.054 \pm 0.021$
	108.2	$+0.052 \pm 0.025$
	98.1	$+0.186 \pm 0.028$
	88.1	$+0.275 \pm 0.028$
	78.1	$+0.384 \pm 0.028$
Carroll (1962)		
128 mev	33.0	0.436 ± 0.066
Abs. error	41.2	0.466 ± 0.039
1 ± 0.04	51.7	0.571 ± 0.041
	61.7	0.588 ± 0.044
	71.8	0.471 ± 0.044
	81.9	0.312 ± 0.051

TABLE A-7 *(Continued)*

Author, Energy	θ cm.	Polarization
Stafford (1962)		
140 ± 2 mev	20.7	0.283 ± 0.027
Abs. error	31.0	0.363 ± 0.018
1 ± 0.04	41.3	0.491 ± 0.022
	61.4	0.593 ± 0.035
	68.0	0.451 ± 0.025
	78.0	0.303 ± 0.027
	88.0	0.232 ± 0.017
	98.0	0.083 ± 0.019
	108.0	0.032 ± 0.013
	118.6	−0.038 ± 0.012
	128.6	−0.044 ± 0.009
	138.7	−0.059 ± 0.009
	149.0	−0.074 ± 0.012
	159.3	−0.037 ± 0.012
Siegel (1956)		
350 mev	46°21′	+0.248 ± 0.031
Abs. error	55°51′	+0.227 ± 0.034
1 ± 0.09	65°29′	+0.075 ± 0.027
	75°13′	−0.039 ± 0.032
	85°7′	−0.273 ± 0.032
	95°9′	−0.210 ± 0.022
	105°20′	−0.246 ± 0.038
	115°41′	−0.213 ± 0.019
	126°8′	−0.289 ± 0.030
	136°45′	−0.147 ± 0.014
	147°28′	−0.132 ± 0.028
	158°15′	−0.106 ± 0.014

TABLE A-8 *pn* POLARIZATION MEASUREMENTS ON
NEUTRONS BOUND IN THE DEUTERON [a]

Author	θ cm.	Polarization	Corrected for Binding Cromer (1963)
Kuckes (1961)			
143 [b] $\pm$ 2 mev	41°	$+0.475 \pm 0.039$	0.526 ± 0.041
Abs. error	51°	$+0.495 \pm 0.017$	0.526 ± 0.020
1 $\pm$ 0.025	62°	$+0.480 \pm 0.016$	0.478 ± 0.019
	72°	$+0.425 \pm 0.021$	0.392 ± 0.023
	82.5°	$+0.272 \pm 0.021$	0.226 ± 0.024
	92.5°	$+0.160 \pm 0.015$	0.111 ± 0.018
	108°	$+0.015 \pm 0.016$	
	118°	-0.020 ± 0.016	
Tinlot (1961)			
215 [b] $\pm$ 2 mev	40	0.469 ± 0.028	
Abs. error	50	0.460 ± 0.031	
1 $\pm$ 0.02	60	0.372 ± 0.041	
	70	0.258 ± 0.033	
	80	0.032 ± 0.036	
	90	-0.069 ± 0.032	
	100	-0.124 ± 0.029	
	110	-0.184 ± 0.029	
	120	-0.170 ± 0.030	
Chamberlain (1957)			
308 [b] mev	21.6	$+0.462 \pm 0.081$	
Abs. error	32.3	$+0.403 \pm 0.048$	
1 $\pm$ 0.04	42.9	$+0.382 \pm 0.036$	
	53.4	$+0.225 \pm 0.028$	
	63.9	$+0.158 \pm 0.030$	
	74.2	-0.012 ± 0.030	
	82.3	-0.090 ± 0.028	
	82.3	-0.126 ± 0.033	
	90.6	-0.097 ± 0.032	
	100.7	-0.238 ± 0.030	
	109.9	-0.249 ± 0.072	
	110.2	-0.261 ± 0.030	
	116.1	-0.228 ± 0.032	
	121.3	-0.255 ± 0.043	
	130.8	-0.222 ± 0.039	

TABLE A-8 (*Continued*)

Author	θ cm.	Polarization	Corrected for Binding Cromer (1963)
	137.3	-0.197 ± 0.026	
	147.7	-0.202 ± 0.029	
	158.4	-0.074 ± 0.023	
	164.9	-0.023 ± 0.035	
Golovin (1959)			
635 mev	$18°$	0.23 ± 0.04	
Read from graph	$34°$	0.29 ± 0.05	
	$45°$	0.18 ± 0.05	
	$56°$	0.07 ± 0.03	
	$66°$	0.02 ± 0.05	
	$90°$	-0.19 ± 0.06	
	$110°$	-0.33 ± 0.04	
	$126°$	-0.29 ± 0.05	

[a] Some values are uncorrected for binding, and binding corrections should be applied according to Cromer (1963).

[b] Energy corrected for binding.

TABLE A-9 *pn* AND *np* TRIPLE SCATTERING PARAMETERS

Author, Energy	θ cm. Parameter	Value	Corrected for Bin 'ing, Cromer (1963)
Hoffman (1962) 137 mev *R*	42.1	$+0.029 \pm 0.080$	$+0.169 \pm 0.089$
	52.5	-0.006 ± 0.082	$+0.080 \pm 0.086$
	62.9	-0.061 ± 0.063	-0.023 ± 0.065
	73.4	-0.160 ± 0.089	-0.151 ± 0.090
	83.6	-0.164 ± 0.207	-0.146 ± 0.207
Hoffman (1962) 135 mev *A*	42.1	$+0.052 \pm 0.072$	-0.020 ± 0.077
	52.5	$+0.123 \pm 0.059$	$+0.070 \pm 0.060$
	62.9	$+0.214 \pm 0.076$	$+0.210 \pm 0.079$
	73.4	$+0.098 \pm 0.095$	$+0.126 \pm 0.096$
	83.6	$+0.496 \pm 0.216$	$+0.532 \pm 0.216$
Warner (1962) 212 mev *D*	40	$+0.70 \pm 0.07$	
	50	$+0.85 \pm 0.08$	
	60	$+0.79 \pm 0.08$	
	70	$+0.99 \pm 0.14$	
	80	$+1.05 \pm 0.45$	
Fischer (1957) 310 mev *D*	42.9	$+0.74 \pm 0.11$	
	63.8	$+0.80 \pm 0.12$	
	63.8	$+0.52 \pm 0.12$	
	82.3	$+0.74 \pm 0.25$	
Fischer (1957) 310 mev *R*	56.7	$+0.61 \pm 0.30$	
	83.9	$+0.28 \pm 0.19$	
Patel (1962) 128 mev D_t	124	-0.12 ± 0.17	
	133	-0.25 ± 0.15	
	142	-0.04 ± 0.15	
	150	-0.01 ± 0.12	
	160	$+0.12 \pm 0.15$	

TABLE A-10 *nn* CROSS SECTION VALUES

Values for neutron-neutron differential cross sections. The data on $I(\theta)$ are Golovin's values for the magnitude of the interference term in scattering of neutrons from deuterium at 300 mev.

Reference	θ	$\sigma\, nn(\theta)$	$I(\theta)$
Dzelepov (1956)			
300 mev	12	7.9 ± 1.5	
	16	6.0 ± 1.0	
	20	4.8 ± 0.7	
	30	3.2 ± 0.6	
	40	3.2 ± 0.6	0.60
	50	3.5 ± 0.8	0.36
	60	3.8 ± 0.6	0.20
	70	3.75 ± 0.6	0.10
	80	3.75 ± 0.6	0.09
	90	3.6 ± 0.8	0.04
Golovin (1956)			
590 mev	30	5.8 ± 0.8	
	49	4.7 ± 0.5	
	55	3.8 ± 0.4	
	67	2.9 ± 0.35	
	78	2.3 ± 0.30	
	89	2.5 ± 0.25	

References

A. Abashian and E. M. Hafner, *Phys. Rev. Letters* **1**, 255 (1958).

A. Abragam, *Phys. Rev. Letters* **1**, 375 (1958).

A. Abragam and W. G. Proctor, *Compt. Rend.* **246**, 2253 (1958).

A. Abragam, M. Borghini, P. Catillon, J. Coustham, P. Roubeau and J. Thirion, *Phys. Rev. Letters* **2**, 310 (1962).

M. Abraham, M. A. H. McCausland and F. N. H. Robinson, *Phys. Rev. Letters* **2**, 449 (1959).

J. V. Allaby, A. Ashmore, A. N. Diddens, J. Eades, G. B. Huxtable and K. Skarsvag, *Proc. Phys. Soc. (London)* **77**, 234 (1961).

J. J. V. Allaby, A. Chisholm, J. Eades and A. N. James, *Phys. Rev. Letters* **3**, 253 (1963).

L. Allen, *Phys. Rev.* **98**, 705 (1955).

I. Alexeff and W. Haeberli, *Nucl. Phys.* **15**, 609 (1960).

E. Amaldi and E. Fermi, *Phys. Rev.* **50**, 899 (1936).

D. Amati, E. Leader and B. Vitale, *Nuovo Cimento* **17**, 68 (1959); **18**, 402, 458 (1960).

N. S. Amoglobeli and Yu M. Kazarinov, *JETP* **33**, 53 (1958); *Sov. Phys. JETP* **7**, 37 (1958).

N. S. Amoglobeli and Yu M. Kazarinov, *JETP* **37**, 1587 (1959); *Sov. Phys.* **10**, 1125 (1960).

N. S. Amoglobeli, B. M. Golovin, Yu M. Kazarinov, S. B. Medved and N. M. Polev; *JETP* **38**, 660 (1960).

N. S. Amoglobeli, Yu M. Kazarinov, S. N. Sokolov and I. N. Silin, *Proc. X Intern. Conf. High Energy Physics*, 64 (1960).

L. S. Anderson, F. M. Pipkin and J. C. Baird, *Phys. Rev.* **120**, 1279 (1960).

Aron, Hoffmann and Williams, UCRL-121 (1951) unpublished.

A. Ashmore, R. G. Jarvis, D. S. Mather and S. K. Sen, *Proc. Phys. Soc. (London)* **A70**, 745 (1957).

A. Ashmore, D. S. Mather and S. K. Sen, *Proc. Phys. Soc. (London)* **A71**, 552 (1958).

A. Ashmore, A. N. Diddens, G. B. Huxtable and K. Skarsvag, *Proc. Phys. Soc. (London)* **72**, 289 (1958); **73**, 957 (1959); **74**, 482 (1959).

G. P. Auffray, *Phys. Rev. Letters* **6**, 120 (1961).

N. Austern, *Phys. Rev.* **92**, 670 (1953).

N. Austern and E. Rost, *Phys. Rev.* **117**, 1506 (1960).

S. A. Azimov, Do In Seb, L. F. Kirillova, E. M. Khabibullina, E. N. Tsyganov, M. G. Shafranova, B. A. Shakhbazyan and A. A. Yuldashev, *JETP* **42**, 430 (1962); *Sov. Phys. JETP* **15**, 299 (1962).

A. R. Baker and D. H. Wilkinson, *Phil. Mag.* **3**, 647 (1958).

W. F. Baker, E. W. Jenkins, A. L. Read, G. Cocconi, V. T. Cocconi and J. Orear, *Phys. Rev. Letters* **9**, 221 (1962).

W. P. Ball, UCRL-1938 (1952) (unpublished).

V. Bargmann, L. Michel and V. L. Telegdi, *Phys. Rev. Letters* **2**, 435 (1959).

P. Bareyre, J. F. Detoef, L. W. Smith, R. D. Tripp and L. Van Rossum, *Nuovo Cimento* **20**, 1049 (1961).

C. A. Barnes, J. H. Carver, G. H. Stafford and D. H. Wilkinson, *Phys. Rev.* **86**, 359 (1952).

C. J. Batty, W. O. Lock and P. V. March, *Proc. Phys. Soc. (London)* **73**, 100 (1959).

C. J. Batty, *Nucl. Phys.* **23**, 562 (1962).

C. J. Batty, G. H. Stafford and R. Gilmore, *Phys. Rev. Letters* **2**, 109 (1962).

R. E. Bell and L. G. Elliott, *Phys. Rev.* **79**, 282 (1950) plus later correction.

W. Benenson, R. L. Walter and T. H. May, *Phys. Rev. Letters* **8**, 66 (1962).

S. Bertozzi, P. T. Demos, S. Kowalski, C. P. Sargent, W. Turchinetz, R. Fullwood and J. Russell, *Phys. Rev. Letters* **10**, 106 (1963).

H. A. Bethe and R. Peierls, *Proc. Roy. Soc. (London)* **A149**, 176 (1935).

H. A. Bethe, *Phys. Rev.* **76**, 38 (1949).

H. A. Bethe and C. Longmire, *Phys. Rev.* **77**, 647 (1950).

H. A. Bethe, *Ann. Phys. (NY)* **3**, 190 (1958).

H. A. Bethe and P. Morrison, *Elementary Nuclear Theory*, Wiley, New York, 1953.

H. Bichsel, R. F. Mozley and W. A. Aron, *Phys. Rev.* **105**, 1788 (1957).

L. Bird, D. N. Edwards, B. Rose, A. E. Taylor and E. Wood, *Nucl. Phys.* **42**, 280 (1963).

L. Bird, D. N. Edwards, B. Rose, A. E. Taylor and E. Wood, *J. Phys. Radium* **21**, 329 (1960).

L. Bird, P. Christmas, A. E. Taylor and E. Wood, *Nucl. Phys.* **27**, 586 (1961).

G. R. Bishop, C. H. Collie, H. Halban, A. Hedgran, K. Siegbahn, S. Du Toit and R. Wilson, *Phys. Rev.* **80**, 211 (1950).

G. R. Bishop and R. Wilson, *Encyclopedia of Physics XLII,* Springer Verlag (1958), p. 309.

W. A. Blanpied and K. N. Brockman, *Phys. Rev.* **116**, 738 (1959).

J. M. Blatt and J. D. Jackson, *Rev. Mod. Phys.* **22**, 77 (1950).

J. M. Blatt and J. D. Jackson, *Phys. Rev.* **76**, 18 (1950).

J. M. Blatt and L. C. Biedenharn, *Phys. Rev.* **86**, 399 (1952).

J. M. Blatt and V. F. Weisskopf, *Theoretical Nuclear Physics,* Wiley, New York, 1952.

R. J. Blin-Stoyle, *Phys. Rev.* **118**, 1605 (1960).

F. Bloch, D. Nicodemus and H. H. Staub, *Phys. Rev.* **74**, 1025 (1948).

F. Boehm and U. Hauser, *Bull. Am. Phys. Soc. II* **4**, 460 (1959).

N. Bogachev and I. Vzorov, *Dokl. Akad. Nauk. SSSR* **99**, 931 (1954); *Dokl. Akad. Nauk. SSST* **99**, 959 (1954).

N. Bogachev, *Dokl. Akad. Nauk. SSSR* **108**, 806 (1956); *Soviet Phys. Doklady* **1**, 361 (1957).

P. H. Bowen, G. C. Cox, G. Huxtable, A. H. Langsford, J. P. Scanlon and J. J. Thresher, *Nucl. Instr.* **15**, 31 (1962).

P. H. Bowen, G. C. Cox, G. B. Huxtable, A. Langsford, J. P. Scanlon and J. J. Thresher, *Phys. Rev. Letters* **7**, 248 (1961).

P. H. Bowen, J. P. Scanlon, G. H. Stafford, J. J. Thresher and P. E. Hodgson, *Nucl. Phys.* **22**, 640 (1961).

P. Bowen, *et al.,* private communication (1962).

G. Breit, *Rev. Mod. Phys.* **23**, 238 (1951).

G. Breit, *Proc. Natl. Acad. Sci. U.S.* **46**, 746 (1960).

G. Breit, *Rev. Mod. Phys.* **94**, 766 (1962).

G. Breit, M. H. Hull, K. E. Lassila and K. D. Pyatt, *Phys. Rev.* **120**, 2227 (1960).

J. G. Brennan and R. G. Sachs, *Phys. Rev.* **88**, 824 (1952).

S. Brimberg, *Kgl. Tek. Hogskol. Stockholm Avhandl.* **116** (1956).

M. J. Brinkworth and B. Rose, *Nuovo Cimento* **3**, 195 (1956).

R. A. Bryan, *Nuovo Cimento* **16**, 895 (1960).

R. M. Brugger, J. E. Evans, E. G. Joki and R. S. Shankland, *Phys. Rev.* **104**, 1054 (1956).

F. Bumiller, M. Crossiaux, E. Dally and R. Hofstadter, *Phys. Rev.* **124**, 1623 (1961).

V. C. Burkig and K. R. MacKenzie, *Phys. Rev.* **106**, 848 (1957).

Cabrespine, *et al., J. Phys. Radium* **21**, 332 (1960).

G. Calame, *et al., Nucl. Instr.* **1**, 169 (1957).

S. Carpenter and R. Wilson, *Phys. Rev.* **113**, 650 (1959).

A. S. Carroll, P. M. Patel, N. Strax and D. Miller, *Phys. Rev.* in press (1963).

L. Castillijo and R. Peierls, *Proc. X Intern. Conf. High Energy Physics,* 64 (1960).

C. Caversazio, K. Kuroda and A. Michaelowicz, *J. Phys. Radium* **22**, 628 (1961)

J. Chadwick and M. Goldhaber, *Proc. Roy. Soc. (London)* **A151**, 479 (1955).

O. Chamberlain, E. Segré and C. Wiegand, *Phys. Rev.* **83**, 923 (1951).

O. Chamberlain, G. Pettingill, E. Segré and C. Wiegand, *Phys. Rev.* **93**, 1424 (1954).

O. Chamberlain and M. G. White, *Phys. Rev.* **95**, 1226 (1954).

O. Chamberlain, E. Segré, R. D. Tripp, C. Wiegand and T. Ypsilantis, *Phys. Rev.* **102**, 1659 (1956).

O. Chamberlain, E. Segré, R. D. Tripp, C. Wiegand and T. Ypsilantis, *Phys. Rev.* **105**, 288 (1957).

F. F. Chen, C. P. Leavitt and A. M. Shapiro, *Phys. Rev.* **103**, 211 (1956).

G. F. Chew and M. L. Goldberger, *Phys. Rev.* **75**, 1637 (1949).

G. F. Chew, *Phys. Rev.* **80**, 710 (1951).

G. F. Chew and G. E. Wick, *Phys. Rev.* **83**, 636 (1952).

G. F. Chew and M. L. Goldberger, *Phys. Rev.* **87**, 778 (1952).

G. F. Chew and F. E. Low, *Phys. Rev.* **113**, 1640 (1959).

R. S. Christian, *Phys. Rev.* **75**, 1675 (1949).

P. Christmas, Rutherford Jubilee Conf. Manchester (1961).

E. L. Chupp, R. W. Jewell and W. John, *Phys. Rev.* **121**, 238 (1961).

G. Cocconi, A. N. Diddens, E. Lillethun, G. Manning, A. E. Taylor, T. G. Walker and A. M. Wetherell, *Phys. Rev. Letters* **7**, 450 (1961).

D. I. Cooper, D. H. Frisch and R. L. Zimmerman, *Phys. Rev.* **94**, 1209 (1954).

T. Coor, D. A. Hill, W. F. Hornyak, L. H. Smith and G. Snow, *Phys. Rev.* **98**, 1369 (1955).

B. Cork and W. Hartsough, *Phys. Rev.* **94**, 1300 (1954).

B. Cork, A. Wenzel and C. M. Causey, *Phys. Rev.* **107**, 859 (1957).

B. Cork, A. Wenzel and C. M. Causey, *Phys. Rev.* **94**, 1300 (1957).

A. M. Cormack, J. N. Palmieri, N. F. Ramsey and R. Wilson, *Phys. Rev.* **115**, 599 (1955).

A. V. Crewe and Gregory, *Proc. Roy Soc. (London)* **A232**, 242 (1955).

A. Cromer, *Phys. Rev.* **113**, 1607 (1959).

A. Cromer and E. Thorndike, *Phys. Rev.* in press (1963).

K. M. Crowe and R. H. Phillips, *Phys. Rev.* **96**, 470 (1954).

P. Cziffra, M. H. MacGregor, M. J. Moravcsik and H. P. Stapp, *Phys. Rev.* **114**, 880 (1959).

P. Cziffra and M. J. Moravcsik, *Phys. Rev.* **116**, 226 (1959).

J. Dabrowski, *Nucl. Phys.* **37**, 647 (1962).

J. Dabrowski and J. Sawicki, *Nucl. Phys.* **22**, 318 (1961); **13**, 621 (1959).

G. von Dardel and N. G. Sjostrand, *Phys. Rev.* **96**, 1245 (1954).

G. von Dardel, D. H. Frisch, R. Memnod, R. H. Milburn, P. A. Pirone, M. Vivargent, G. Weber and K. Winter, *Phys. Rev. Letters* **5**, 333 (1960).

R. B. Day, L. L. Mills, J. B. Perry, Jr. and F. Scherb, *Phys. Rev.* **98**, 279 (1955).

J. DeJuren and N. Knable, *Phys. Rev.* **77**, 606 (1950).

W. C. Dickinson, L. Passell and O. Halpern, *Phys. Rev.* **126**, 632 (1962).

J. Dickson and D. C. Salter, *Nuovo Cimento* **6**, 235 (1957).

A. N. Diddens, E. Lillethun, G. Manning, A. E. Taylor, T. G. Walker and A. M. Wetherell, *Phys. Rev. Letters* **9**, 32, 108, 111 (1962).

A. Donnachie, *Nucl. Phys.* **32**, 637 (1962).

J. D. Dowell, W. R. Frisken, G. Martelli, B. Musgrave, H. B. van der Raay and R. Rubinstein, *Nuovo Cimento* **18**, 818 (1960).

S. Drell and Zachariasen, *Electromagnetic Structure of Nucleons*, Oxford University Press (1961).

D. J. Drickey and L. N. Hand, *Phys. Rev. Letters* **9**, 521 (1962).

L. Durand III, *Phys. Rev.* **108**, 1597 (1957); *Phys. Rev.* **123**, 1393 (1961).

V. P. Dzhelepov, B. M. Golovin, Yu M. Kazarirov and Semenov, *Dokl. Akad. Nauk. SSSR* **99**, 943 (1954).

V. P. Dzhelepov, Moskalev and S. B. Medved, *Dokl. Akad. Nauk. SSSR* **104**, 380 (1955).

V. P. Dzhelepov, Satarov and B. M. Golovin, *Dokl. Akad. Nauk. SSSR* **104**, 717 (1955).

J. W. Easley, UCRL-2693 (1954) unpublished.

C. E. Engelke, R. E. Benenson, E. Melkonian and J. M. Lebowitz, *Phys. Rev.* **129**, 324 (1963).

A. C. England, W. A. Gibson, K. Gotow, E. Heer and J. Tinlot, *Phys. Rev.* **124**, 561 (1961).

E. Engels, T. Bowen, J. W. Cronin, R. L. McIlwain and L. G. Pondrom, *Phys. Rev.* **129**, 1858 (1963).

M. J. Esten, T. C. Griffith, G. J. Lush, A. J. Metheringham and C. P. Van Zyl, *Nuclear Forces and the 2 Nucleon Problem*, Pergamon (1960), p. 277.

A. Everett, *Phys. Rev.* **126**, 831 (1962).

F. Everling, A. Konig, J. H. E. Mattauch and A. H. Wapstra, *Nucl. Data Tables*, Part 1.

D. Feldman, *Phys. Rev.* **89**, 1159 (1953).

H. Feshbach and J. Schwinger, *Phys. Rev.* **84**, 194 (1951).

H. Feshbach, E. Lomon and A. Tubis, *Phys. Rev. Letters* **6**, 635 (1961).

R. E. Fields, R. L. Becker and R. K. Adair, *Phys. Rev.* **94**, 389 (1954).

D. Fischer and G. Golbhaber, *Phys. Rev.* **95**, 1350 (1954).

D. Fischer, UCRL-3281 (1957).

E. R. Flynn and P. J. Bendt, *Phys. Rev.* **128**, 1268 (1963).

L. L. Foldy and E. Eriksen, *Phys. Rev.* **98**, 775 (1955).

J. Friedman, H. Kendall and P. A. M. Gram, *Phys. Rev.* **120**, 992 (1960).

S. Fubini, *Phys. Rev. Letters* **7**, 466 (1961).

J. A. Galey, *Phys. Rev.* **117**, 763 (1960).

J. L. Gammel and R. M. Thaler, *Progress in Nuclear Physics* (1959).

Gelfand, Frashian, Ivanova, Pomeranchuk and Smorodinskii, read by Tyapkin, *Proc. X Intern. Conf. High Energy Physics*, 138 (1960).

G. Gerstein, thesis, Harvard University (1957).

G. Gerstein, J. Niederer and K. Strauch, *Phys. Rev.* **108**, 427 (1957).

S. Glashow, *Phys. Rev. Letters* **7**, 469 (1961).

A. E. Glassgold, *Progr. Nucl. Phys.* **7**, Pergamon Press (1959).

R. J. Glauber, *Physica* **22**, 1185 (1956).

N. K. Glendenning and G. Kramer, *Phys. Rev.* **126**, 2159 (1962).

M. L. Goldberger, Y. Nambu and R. Oehme, *Ann. Phys.* (*NY*) **2**, 226 (1957).

R. Goloskie and J. N. Palmieri, private communication (1962).

R. Goloskie and K. Strauch, *Nucl. Phys.* **29**, 474 (1962).

B. M. Golovin, V. P. Dzhelepov, Yu M. Katyshev, A. D. Konin and S. V. Medvedev, Joint Institute for Nuclear Research (1958), p. 243.

B. M. Golovin, V. P. Dzhelepov, V. S. Kadzedzin and V. N. Satarov, *Acad. Nauk. SSSR* **36**, 433 (1959).

B. M. Golovin, V. P. Dzhelepov, Yu. M. Katyshev, A. D. Konin and S. V. Medved, *JETP* **36**, 735 (1959); *Sov. Phys. JETP* **9**, 516 (1959).

B. M. Golovin, *et al.*, report p. 236 (1959).

B. M. Golovin, R. Ya. Zulkarneev and V. P. Dzhelepov, *Proc. X. Intern. Conf. High Energy Physics* **115** (1960).

B. M. Golovin, V. P. Dzhelepov and R. Ya. Zulkarneev, *JETP* **41**, 83 (1961); *Sov. Phys. JETP* **14**, 63 (1962).

P. Gorenstein, D. Luckey and L. Osborne, *Bull. Am. Phys. Soc. II* **8**, 36 (1963).

K. Gotow, F. Lobkowicz and Ernst Heer, *Phys. Rev.* **127**, 2206 (1962).

K. Gotow, private communication (1962).

T. C. Griffith, D. C. Imrie, G. J. Lush and A. J. Metheringham, *Phys. Rev. Letters* **10**, 444 (1963).

F. T. Hadjioannou, *Phys. Rev.* **125**, 1414 (1962).

F. T. Hadjioannou, R. J. N. Phillips and W. Rarita, *Phys. Rev. Letters* **9**, 183 (1962).

E. M. Hafner, W. F. Hornyak, C. E. Falk, G. Snow and T. Coor, *Phys. Rev.* **89**, 204 (1953).

E. M. Hafner, *Phys. Rev.* **111**, 297 (1958).

B. Hamermesh, G. R. Ringo and S. Wexler, *Phys. Rev.* **90**, 603 (1953).

T. Hamada, *Progr. Theoret. Phys.* (*Kyoto*) **25**, 247 (1961).

L. Hand, D. G. Miller and R. Wilson, *Phys. Rev. Letters* **8**, 110 (1962).

L. Hand, D. G. Miller and R. Wilson, *Rev. Mod. Phys.* **35**, 335 (1963).

R. S. Harding, *Phys. Rev.* **111**, 1164 (1958).

S. P. Harris, C. O. Muelhouse, D. Rose, H. P. Schroeder, G. E. Thomas and S. Wexler, *Phys. Rev.* **91**, 125 (1953).

D. Harting, J. R. Holt and J. A. Moore, *Proc. Phys. Soc. (London)* **71**, 770 (1958).

A. J. Hartzler and R. T. Siegel, *Phys. Rev.* **95**, 185 (1954).

A. J. Hartzler, R. T. Siegel and W. Opitz, *Phys. Rev.* **95**, 591 (1954).

W. W. Havens and L. J. Rainwater, *Phys. Rev.* **75**, 1296A (1949).

Hecks and A. J. Kirschbaum, Livermore report MTA 28 (1952).

S. Hee and E. H. Thorndike, *Phys. Rev.* in press (1963).

L. Heller, *Phys. Rev.* **120**, 627 (1960).

L. R. Henrich, D. C. Sewell and J. Vale, *Rev. Sci. Instr.* **20**, 887 (1949).

A. Herzenberg and E. J. Squires, *Nuclear Forces and the Few Nucleon Problem,* Pergamon (1960), p. 249.

W. N. Hess, *Rev. Mod. Phys.* **30**, 364 (1954).

P. Hillman, R. H. Stahl and N. F. Ramsey, *Phys. Rev.* **96**, 115 (1954).

P. Hillman, A. Johansson and G. Tibell, *Phys. Rev.* **110**, 1210 (1958).

R. K. Hobbie and D. Miller, *Phys. Rev.* **120**, 2201 (1960).

R. Hoffman, J. Lefrançois, E. H. Thorndike and R. Wilson, *Phys. Rev.* **125**, 973 (1962).

R. Hoffman, J. Lefrançois and E. H. Thorndike, *Phys. Rev.* in press (1963).

R. Hofstadter, *Rev. Mod. Phys.* **28**, 214 (1956).

R. Hofstadter, *Ann. Rev. Nucl. Sci.* **7**, 231 (1957).

J. R. Holt, J. C. Kluyver and J. A. Moore, *Proc. Phys. Soc. (London)* **71**, 781 (1958).

R. J. Homer, W. K. McFarlane, A. W. O'Dell, E. J. Sacharidis and G. H. Eaton, *Nuovo Cimento* **23**, 690 (1962).

D. J. Hughes, M. T. Burgy and G. R. Ringo, *Phys. Rev.* **77**, 291 (1950).

D. J. Hughes, *Neutron Optics,* Addison Wesley, New York, 1953.

D. J. Hughes and J. A. Harvey, Neutron Cross Sections 2nd ed. BNL-325, U. S. Government Printing Office (1955).

M. H. Hull, K. Lassila, H. Ruppel, F. McDonald and G. Breit, *Phys. Rev.* **122**, 1606 (1961).

L. Hulthèn and M. Sugawara, *Encyclopedia of Physics, XXXI9,* Springer Verlag, Berlin (1957).

C. F. Hwang, T. R. Ophel, E. Thorndike and R. Wilson, *Phys. Rev.* **119**, 352 (1960).

C. F. Hwang, D. H. Nordby, S. Suwa and J. H. Williams, *Phys. Rev. Letters* **9**, 104 (1962).

K. Ilakovac, L. G. Kuo, M. Petravic, I. Slaus and P. Tomas, *Phys. Rev. Letters* **6**, 356 (1961); and Rutherford Jubilee Conf. Manchester (1961).

J. D. Jackson and J. M. Blatt, *Rev. Mod. Phys.* **22**, 96 (1950).

M. Jacob and G. C. Wick, *Ann. Phys. (NY)* **7**, 404 (1959).

B. A. Jacobsohn, *Phys. Rev.* **89**, 881 (1953).

V. K. Jankus, *Phys. Rev.* **102**, 1586 (1956); and thesis, Stanford University (1956).

O. N. Jarvis, B. Rose, J. Scanlon, E. Wood, *Nucl. Phys.* **42**, 294 (1963).

T. H. Jeong, L. H. Johnston, D. E. Young and C. N. Waddell, *Phys. Rev.* **118**, 1080 (1960).

A. Johansson, G. Tibbell, K. Parker and P. E. Hodgson, *Nucl. Phys.* **21**, 383 (1960).

L. H. Johnston and D. A. Swenson, *Phys. Rev.* **111**, 212 (1958).

L. H. Johnston and Y. S. Tsai, *Phys. Rev.* **115**, 1293 (1959).

L. H. Johnston and D. E. Young, *Phys. Rev.* **116**, 989 (1959).

D. P. Jones, P. L. O'Neill and P. B. Murphy, *Proc. Roy. Soc. (London)* **72**, 429 (1958).

H. F. Jones, *Nuovo Cimento* **26**, 790 (1962).

J. A. Kane, R. A. Stallwood, R. B. Sutton, T. H. Fields and J. G. Fox, *Phys. Rev.* **95**, 1694 (1954).

Yu M. Kazarinov and Yu N. Simonov, *JETP* **31**, 169 (1956); *Sov. Phys. JETP* **4**, 161 (1957); *JETP* **43**, 35 (1963); *Sov. Phys. JETP* **16**, 24 (1963).

Yu M. Kazarinov, V. S. Kiselev, I. N. Silin and S. N. Sokolov, *JETP* **41** (1961); *Sov. Phys. JETP* **14**, 143 (1962).

Yu M. Kazarinov and I. N. Silin, Dubna reports P944, P970, P1011; also *XI Intern. Conf. on High Energy Physics* (1962).

A. H. Kazi, N. C. Rasmussen and H. Mark, *Phys. Rev.* **123**, 1310 (1961).

J. C. Keck and A. V. Tollestrup, *Phys. Rev.* **101**, 360 (1956).

R. Keller, L. Dick and M. Fidecaro, *Compt. rend.* **248**, 3154 (1959).

J. Kellogg, I. Rabi, N. F. Ramsey and J. Zacharias, *Phys. Rev.* **56**, 728 (1939); **57**, 677 (1940).

E. Kelly, C. Leith, E. Segrè and C. Wiegand, *Phys. Rev.* **79**, 96 (1951).

H. Kendall, J. Friedman, E. F. Erickson and P. A. M. Gram, *Phys. Rev.* **124**, 1596 (1961).

A. F. Kerman, H. McManus and R. Thaler, *Ann. Phys. (NY)* **8**, 551 (1959).

R. W. King, *Rev. Mod. Phys.* **26**, 327 (1954).

A. J. Kirshbaum, UCRL-1967 (1954) (unpublished).

D. J. Knecht, S. Messelt, E. D. Berners and L. C. Northcliffe, *Phys. Rev.* **114**, 550 (1959).

J. W. Knowles, *Can. J. Phys.* **40**, 257 (1962).

W. C. Koehler and E. W. Wollan, *Phys. Rev.* **85**, 491 (1952).

H. G. Kolsky, T. E. Phipps, N. F. Ramsey and H. B. Silsbee, *Phys. Rev.* **87**, 395 (1952).

K. L. Kowalski and D. Feldman, *Phys. Rev.* **130**, 276 (1963).

U. E. Kruse, J. M. Teem and N. F. Ramsey, *Phys. Rev.* **101**, 1079 (1956).

A. F. Kuckes, R. Wilson and P. F. Cooper, Jr., *Ann. Phys. (NY)* **15**, 193 (1961).

A. F. Kuckes and R. Wilson, *Phys. Rev.* **121**, 1226 (1961).

Yu Kumekin, M. G. Mesheryakov, S. B. Nursukev and G. D. Stoletov, *JETP* **35**, 1398 (1958); *Proc. XI Intern. Conf. High Energy Physics* (1962).

P. Kusch, *Phys. Rev.* **100**, 1188 (1955).

R. Larsen, private communication (1962).

K. E. Lassila, M. H. Hull, H. M. Ruppell, F. A. MacDonald and G. Breit, *Phys. Rev.* **126**, 881 (1962).

M. E. Law, G. W. Hutchinson and D. H. White, *Nucl. Phys.* **9**, 600 (1959).

K. J. LeCouteur, *Proc. Roy. Soc. (London)* **A232**, 236 (1955).

B. A. Lippmann and J. S. Schwinger, *Phys. Rev.* **79**, 469 (1950).

F. Lobkowicz and E. H. Thorndike, *Rev. Sci. Instr.* **33**, 454 (1962).

F. Lobkowitz and K. Gotow, *Phys. Rev.* in press (1962).

M. J. Longo, J. A. Helland, W. N. Hess, B. J. Moyer and V. Perez-Mendez, *Phys. Rev. Letters* **3**, 568 (1959).

M. H. MacGregor, M. J. Moravcsik and H. P. Stapp, *Ann. Rev. Nucl. Sci.* **10**, 291 (1960).

M. H. MacGregor, M. J. Moravcsik and H. P. Noyes, *Phys. Rev.* **123**, 1835 (1961).

J. A. MacIntyre and S. Dhar, *Phys. Rev.* **106**, 1074 (1957).

J. A. MacIntyre and G. R. Burleson, *Phys. Rev.* **112**, 2077 (1958).

M. H. MacGregor, *Phys. Rev.* **123**, 2154 (1961).

W. K. McFarlane, R. J. Homer, A. W. O'Dell, E. J. Sacharidis and G. H. Eaton, private communication (1962, 1963).

R. S. McKean, *Phys. Rev.* **125**, 1399 (1962).

L. Marshall and J. Marshall, *Phys. Rev.* **98**, 1398 (1955).

P. Marin, G. R. Bishop and H. Halban, *Proc. Phys. Soc. (London)* **A67**, 608 (1953).

G. Martelli, H. B. Van de Raay, R. Rubinstein, K. R. Chapman, J. D. Dowell, W. R. Frisken, B. Musgrave and D. H. Reading, *Nuovo Cimento* **21**, 581 (1961).

W. R. McMurray and C. H. Collie, *Proc. Phys. Soc. (London)* **A68**, 181 (1955).

R. E. Meads, C. J. England, C. H. Collie and G. C. Weeks, *Proc. Phys. Soc. (London)* **A69**, 469 (1956).

E. Melkonian, *Phys. Rev.* **76**, 1744, 1750 (1949).

M. G. Mescheryakov, Bogachev, Soroko and Vzorov, *Izvest. Acad. Nauk. SSSR* **99**, 959 (1954).

M. G. Mescheryakov, Bogachev and Neganov, *Izvest. Acad. Nauk. SSSR* **19**, 548 (1955).

M. G. Mescheryakov, S. B. Nuruskev and G. D. Stoletov, *Sov. Phys. JETP* **4**, 337 (1957).

M. G. Mescheryakov, S. B. Nureshev and G. D. Stoletov, *JETP* **33**, 37 (1957); *Sov. Phys.* **6**, 28 (1958).

G. P. Millburn, W. Birnbaum, W. E. Crandall and L. Schechter, *Phys. Rev.* **95**, 1268 (1954).

D. G. Miller and Russell Hobbie, *Rev. Sci. Instr.* **31**, 621 (1960).

R. C. Mobley and R. A. Laubenstein, *Phys. Rev.* **80**, 309 (1950).

J. E. Monahan, S. Raburg and C. C. Trail, *Nucl. Phys.* **24**, 400 (1961).

M. J. Moravcsik, *The Two Nucleon Problem,* Oxford University Press (1962).

G. R. Mott, G. L. Guernsey and B. K. Nelson, *Phys. Rev.* **88**, 9 (1952).

N. F. Mott and H. S. W. Massey, *Theory of Atomic Collisions,* Oxford University Press (1933), ch. II.

H. T. Motz, R. E. Carter and P. C. Fisher, *Bull. Am. Phys. Soc. II* **4**, 447 (1959).

V. O. Nicolai, *Rev. Sci. Instr.* **26**, 1203 (1955).

Nikitin, Selektor, Bogomolov and Zombkovsky, *Nuovo Cimento* **7**, 1269 (1955).

K. Nishimura, J. Sanada, S. Kobayashi, K. Fukunaga, N. Ryu, H. Hasai, D. C. Worth, H. Imada, Y. Hiratate and T. Hasegawa, *Prog. Theor. Phys.* (*Tokyo*) in press (1963).

J. C. Noyes, J. E. van Hoomissen, W. C. Miller and B. Waldman, *Phys. Rev.* **95**, 396 (1954).

H. P. Noyes and D. Y. Wong, *Phys. Rev. Letters* **3**, 191 (1959).

H. P. Noyes, *Proc. X Intern. Conf. High Energy Physics,* 138 (1960).

H. P. Noyes, *Phys. Rev.* in press (1962).

H. Palevsky, J. A. Moore, R. L. Stearns, H. R. Muether, R. J. Sutter, R. E. Chrien, A. P. Jain and K. Otnes, *Phys. Rev. Letters* **9**, 509 (1962).

J. N. Palmieri, A. M. Cormack, N. F. Ramsey and R. Wilson, *Ann. Phys.* (*NY*) **5**, 299 (1958).

J. Palmieri and E. E. Prenowitz, private communication (1962).

J. de Pangher, *Phys. Rev.* **99**, 1447 (1955).

P. M. Patel, A. Carroll, N. Strax and D. G. Miller, *Phys. Rev. Letters* **8**, 491 (1962).

D. M. van Patter and W. Whaling, *Rev. Mod. Phys.* **26**, 402 (1956).

R. B. Perkins and J. E. Simmons, *Phys. Rev.* **130**, 272 (1963).

J. K. Perring, *Nucl. Phys.* **42**, 306 (1963).

G. A. Peterson and W. E. Barber, Rutherford Jubilee Conference (1961).

H. L. Poss, E. D. Salant, G. A. Snow and L. C. L. Yuan, *Phys. Rev.* **87**, 11 (1952).

H. Postma and R. Wilson, *Phys. Rev.* **121**, 1229 (1961).

R. V. Pound, private communication.

W. M. Preston, R. Wilson and J. C. Street, *Phys. Rev.* **118**, 579 (1960).

Y. D. Prokoshkin, V. I. Rykalin and I. M. Vasilevski, Report D-678 (1961).

L. D. Pushikov, R. Ryndin and Ia Smorodinskii, *J. Exptl. Theoret. Phys. USSR* **32**, 592 (1956); *Sov. Phys. JETP* **5**, 489 (1957).

T. C. Randle, A. E. Taylor and E. Wood, *Proc. Roy. Soc. (London)* **A213**, 392 (1952).

T. C. Randle, private communication (1956).

L. A. Rayburn and E. O. Wollan, *Phys. Rev.* **87**, 174A (1952).

Lord Rayleigh, *Theory of Sound* **ii**, 323 (1877).

Riazuddin, *Nucl. Phys.* **7**, 217, 223 (1958).

M. Rich and R. Madey, UCRL-2301 (1954) unpublished.

W. B. Riesenfeld and K. M. Watson, *Phys. Rev.* **102**, 1157 (1956).

G. R. Ringo, M. T. Burgy and D. J. Hughes, *Phys. Rev.* **84**, 1160 (1951).

M. L. Rustgi, W. Zernick, G. Breit and D. J. Andrews, *Phys. Rev.* **120**, 1881 (1960). Corrected by W. Zickendraht, D. J. Andrews, M. L. Rustig, W. Zernik, A. J. Torruella and G. Breit, *Phys. Rev.* **124**, 1538 (1961).

R. G. Sachs and N. Austern, *Phys. Rev.* **81**, 705 (1951).

R. G. Sachs, *Nuclear Theory*, Addison-Wesley, Reading, Mass. (1955).

A. M. Sachs, *Phys. Rev.* in press (1962).

V. Sailor, private communication (1962).

G. L. Salmon, *Nucl. Phys.* **21**, 15 (1960).

E. E. Salpeter, *Phys. Rev.* **82**, 60 (1951).

R. M. Sanders, *Phys. Rev.* **104**, 1434 (1956).

J. P. Scanlon, G. H. Stafford, J. J. Thresher and P. H. Bowen, *Rev. Sci. Instr.* **28**, 749 (1947).

T. J. Schmugge and C. D. Jeffries, *Phys. Rev. Letters* **9**, 268 (1962).

J. S. Schwinger, *Phys. Rev.* **72**, 742A (1947).

J. S. Schwinger, *Phys. Rev.* **73**, 407 (1948).

J. S. Schwinger, *Phys. Rev.* **78**, 13 (1950).

Selector, Nikitin, Bogomolov and Zombkovsky, *Dokl. Acad. Nauk. SSSR* **99**, 967 (1954).

A. M. Sessler and H. M. Foley, *Phys. Rev.* **110**, 995 (1958).

C. G. Shull, E. O. Wollan, G. A. Morton and W. L. Davidson, *Phys. Rev.* **73**, 842 (1958).

R. T. Siegel, A. J. Hartzler and W. A. Love, *Phys. Rev.* **101**, 838 (1956).

P. Signell, *Phys. Rev. Letters* **5**, 474 (1960).

P. Signell, private communication (1962).

J. E. Simmons, *Phys. Rev.* **104**, 416 (1956).

L. M. Smith, A. W. McReynolds and G. Snow, *Phys. Rev.* **97**, 1186 (1955).

M. Sobel and A. Cromer, *Phys. Rev.* in press (1963).

H. Sommer, H. A. Thomas and H. A. Hipple, *Phys. Rev.* **82,** 697 (1951).

R. B. Sutton, G. H. Fields, J. G. Fox, J. A. Kane, W. E. Mott and R. A. Stallwood, *Phys. Rev.* **97,** 783 (1955).

G. L. Squires and A. T. Stewart, *Phys. Rev.* **90,** 1125 (1953).

G. L. Squires and A. T. Stewart, *Proc. Roy. Soc. (London)* **A230,** 19 (1955).

G. H. Stafford, C. Whitehead and P. Hillman, *Nuovo Cimento* **5,** 1589 (1957).

G. H. Stafford, J. M. Dickson, D. C. Salter and M. K. Craddock, *Nucl. Instr.* **15,** 146 (1962).

G. H. Stafford and C. Whitehead, *Proc. Phys. Soc. (London)* (1962).

R. H. Stahl and N. F. Ramsey, *Phys. Rev.* **96,** 1310 (1954).

D. Stairs, R. Wilson and P. F. Cooper, *Phys. Rev.* **129,** 1672 (1963).

H. P. Stapp, UCRL-8859 (1956) unpublished.

H. P. Stapp, T. J. Ypsilantis and N. Metropolis, *Phys. Rev.* **105,** 32 (1957).

D. Steinberg, Thesis, Harvard University (1961).

R. M. Sternheimer, *Phys. Rev.* **115,** 137 (1959); **118,** 1045 (1960).

C. L. Storrs and D. H. Frisch, *Phys. Rev.* **95,** 1252 (1954).

M. Sugawara, *Progr. Theoret. Phys. (Kyoto)* **14,** 535 (1955).

M. Sugawara, *Phys. Rev.* **117,** 614 (1960).

R. B. Sutton, T. H. Fields, J. G. Fox, J. A. Kane, W. E. Mott and R. A. Stallwood, *Phys. Rev.* **97,** 783 (1955).

J. J. deSwart and R. E. Marshak, *Phys. Rev.* **111,** 272 (1958).

S. Tamor, *Phys. Rev.* **97,** 1077 (1955).

A. E. Taylor and E. Wood, *Phil. Mag.* **44,** 95 (1952).

A. E. Taylor and E. Wood, *Proc. Phys. Soc. (London)* **A69,** 645 (1956).

A. E. Taylor, E. Wood and L. Bird, *Nucl. Phys.* **16,** 320 (1956).

A. E. Taylor, *Rept. Progr. Phys.* **20,** 86 (1957).

A. E. Taylor and E. Wood, *Nucl. Phys.* **25,** 642 (1961).

J. Teem, Thesis, Harvard University (1954).

E. Thorndike and T. R. Ophel, *Phys. Rev.* **119,** 362 (1960).

E. Thorndike, J. Lefrançois and R. Wilson, *Phys. Rev.* **120,** 1819 (1960).

E. H. Thorndike, private communication (1961).

E. H. Thorndike, *Phys. Rev.* **127,** 251 (1962).

J. Tinlot and R. E. Warner, *Phys. Rev.* **124,** 890 (1961).

J. L. Tuck and L. C. Teng, *Phys. Rev.* **305** (1951).

M. Tuve, N. Heydenburg and L. Hafstad, *Phys. Rev.* **50,** 806 (1936).

I. M. Vasilevsky, V. V. Vishnyzkov, E. I. Iliescu and A. A. Tyapkin, *JETP* **12,** 616 (1961).

R. G. P. Voss, J. J. Thresher, C. P. Van Zyl and R. Wilson, *Rev. Sci. Instr.* (1954).

R. G. P. Voss, J. J. Thresher and R. Wilson, *Proc. Roy. Soc. (London)* **A229,** 493 (1955).

R. G. P. Voss and R. Wilson, *Proc. Roy. Soc. (London)* **A236,** 41 (1956).

R. G. P. Voss and R. Wilson, *Phil. Mag.* **47,** 175 (1956).

A. H. Wapstra, *Physica* **21,** 367 (1955).

A. H. Wapstra, *Proc. Intern. Conf. Nuclidic Masses,* 535 (1961).

R. E. Warner and J. H. Tinlot, *Phys. Rev.* **125,** 1028 (1962).

E. A. Whalin, B. D. Schnever and A. O. Hanson, *Phys. Rev.* **101,** 377 (1956).

T. O. White, F. F. Liu, F. J. Loeffler and T. R. Palfrey, *Bull. Am. Phys. Soc. II* **8,** 36 (1963).

C. Whitehead, S. Tornabene and G. H. Stafford, *Proc. Phys. Soc. (London)* **75,** 345 (1960).

E. Wigner, *Phys. Rev.* **43,** 252 (1933).

E. Wigner, *Z. Phys.* **83,** 253 (1953).

D. H. Wilkinson, *Phys. Rev.* **86,** 373 (1952).

D. H. Wilkinson *et al., Phil. Mag.* **6,** 171 (1961).

R. Wilson, *Phys. Rev.* **114,** 260 (1959).

R. Wilson, *J. Phys. Radium* **22,** 610 (1961).

T. F. Wimmett, *Phys. Rev.* **91,** 499 (1953).

L. Wolfenstein, *Ann. Rev. Nucl. Sci.* **6,** 43 (1956).

D. Y Wong and H. P. Noyes, *Phys. Rev.* **126,** 1866 (1962).

D. E. Young and L. H. Johnston, *Phys. Rev.* **119,** 313 (1960).

C. P. Van Zyl, R. G. P. Voss and R. Wilson, *Phil. Mag.* **1,** 1003 (1956).

W. Zickendraht, D. J. Andrews, M. L. Rustig, W. Zernik, A. J. Torruella and G. Breit, *Phys. Rev.* **124,** 1539 (1961).

R. Yu Zulkarneev and I. N. Silin, Dubna report D1107 (1962), unpublished.

A. Ashmore, W. H. Range, R. T. Taylor, B. M. Townes, L. Castillejo and R. F. Peierls, *Nucl. Phys.* **36,** 258 (1962).

G. Breit, *Phys. Rev.* **51,** 248 (1937); **53,** 153 (1937).

G. Breit and R. L. Gluckstern, *Ann. Rev. Nucl. Sci.* **II,** 365 (1953).

G. Breit, M. H. Hull, F. A. McDonald and H. M. Ruppell, *High Energy Physics Conf. CERN* (1962).

G. Breit, M. H. Hull, K. E. Lassila, H. M. Ruppell, *Phys. Rev.* **128,** 826, 830 (1962).

V. A. Bull and D. A. Garbutt, *Phys. Rev.* **130,** 1182 (1963).

G. C. Cox, G. B. Huxtable, J. P. Scanlon and J. J. Thresher, *Nucl. Inst.* **15,** 31 (1963).

D. E. Frederic, *Phys. Rev.* **130,** 1131 (1963).

T. Fujii, G. B. Chadwick, G. B. Collins, P. J. Duke, N. Hien, M. A. R. Kemp and F. Turkot, *Phys. Rev.* **128,** 1836 (1962).

N. Hoshizaki, S. Otzuki, R. Tawagaki and W. Watani, to be published (1963).

E. Marquit, *Phys. Rev. Letters* **1,** 41 (1962).

Nisimura, Sanada, Kobayashi, Fukunaka, Ryu, Hasai, Worth, Imada, Hira-
    date and Hasegawa, to be published (1963).

R. Oehme, *Phys. Rev.* **98,** 147, 216 (1954).

L. Wolfenstein, *Phys. Rev.* **85,** 947 (1952) ; **96,** 1654 (1954) ; **101,** 427 (1956).

E. W. Wollan, private communication (1962). See also Hughes (1955).

Index